KU-350-651

GROOVY GADGETS

Steve Parker

p

This is a Parragon Book
First published in 2000

Parragon
Queen Street House
4 Queen Street
Bath BA1 1HE, UK

ISBN 0-75253-674-5

Printed in Dubai, U.A.E

Produced by
Monkey Puzzle Media Ltd
Gissing's Farm
Fressingfield
Suffolk IP21 5SH
UK

Illustrations: Studio Liddell
Designer: Tim Mayer
Cover design: Victoria Webb
Editor: Linda Sonntag
Editorial assistance: Lynda Lines and Jenny Siklós
Indexer: Caroline Hamilton
Project manager: Katie Orchard

Photos supplied by Tony Stone Images 11 (Bruce Ayres), 24 (Stephen Johnson), 31 (Arthur Tilley), 42 (Jon Riley), and MPM Images.

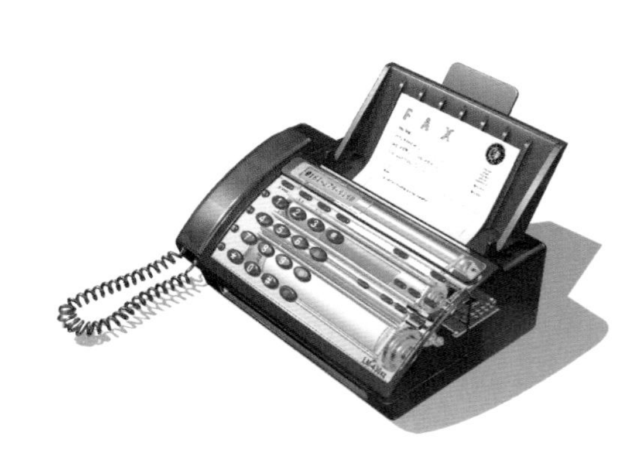

CONTENTS

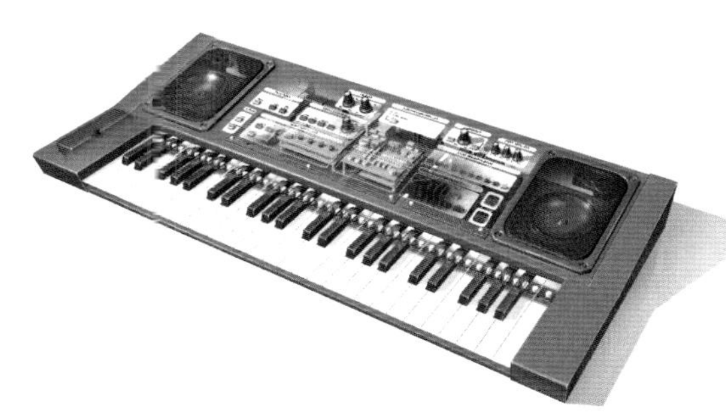

GADGET CRAZY

The twenty-first century is the Age of the Gadget. Never before have we had so many small machines, devices, bits of kit and equipment for use in daily life. Imagine a row of gadgets that includes TV and hi-fi remote controls, a miniature television, a mobile phone, a palmtop or notebook computer, a personal stereo, a satellite navigation receiver, a small computer games console, the latest mini-camcorder and a voice recorder (dictaphone). They are all small plastic cases with displays and buttons and easily slip into the pocket. At first glance you could hardly tell the difference between them. But they are very different. Some are taken apart in this book to explain how they work and what they do.

DEPENDING ON GADGETS

These gadgets and larger ones such as the video cassette player, widescreen TV, microwave oven and hi-fi music system, also shown on the following pages, are designed to make our daily life easier, quicker and more convenient. But we may come to depend on them so much that they cause more problems than they solve! Losing the remote control for the TV or being unable to log on to the Internet might seem like the end of the world. However we somehow manage to get by, usually by getting another gadget.

PROFESSIONAL GADGETS

Some potentially life-saving devices and pieces of machinery are also featured in this book. They include medical scanners for diagnosing diseases and the satellite navigation system, which helps people at sea or in remote areas of land to reach safety. There are also many office gadgets that speed along business, such as the computer, fax machine, image scanner and videophone. The power drill is an example of a gadget that makes physical work easier, more controlled and more precise.

Telecom system
Tele-communications means sending knowledge and information over long distances. It could be two people chatting on the phone, or several networked computers sending vast lists of numbers about bank accounts and business finances. The telecom system is immensely complex and involves huge amounts of old and new technology, from metal wires strung along poles to the latest fibre-optic cables, satellites, microwave links and computerized line exchanges.

It seems real

Virtual reality is becoming more real each year. The headsets, earphones, sensors and other systems get faster and more accurate. VR is not just an electronic toy for the games arcade. It is used in many professions for simulations that train experts such as pilots, surgeons and racing drivers.

GADGETS FOR FUN

Another group of gadgets includes those used mainly for fun, pleasure, creative pastimes and art. Examples are the music synthesizer, the virtual reality headset and the Go-Ped engine-powered scooter. They allow people to use their skills and talents to entertain and amaze us. Without all these gadgets, from the smallest in-ear radio, mobile phone or TV spectacles to massive computer networks and the global telecom system, the world would be less safe, less convenient, less accessible, less interesting – and less fun!

Compact disc revolution

We still have huge libraries filled with books. We still have large rolls of cinema film in bucket-sized cans for the latest feature movie. We still have cupboards full of games, from chess to fight-the-alien. But we can put all of these, and more, on to a compact disc that is read by a laser beam.

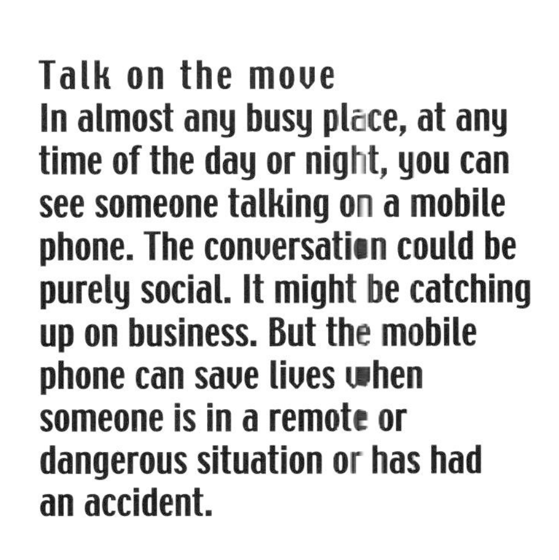

Talk on the move

In almost any busy place, at any time of the day or night, you can see someone talking on a mobile phone. The conversation could be purely social. It might be catching up on business. But the mobile phone can save lives when someone is in a remote or dangerous situation or has had an accident.

MOBILE PHONE

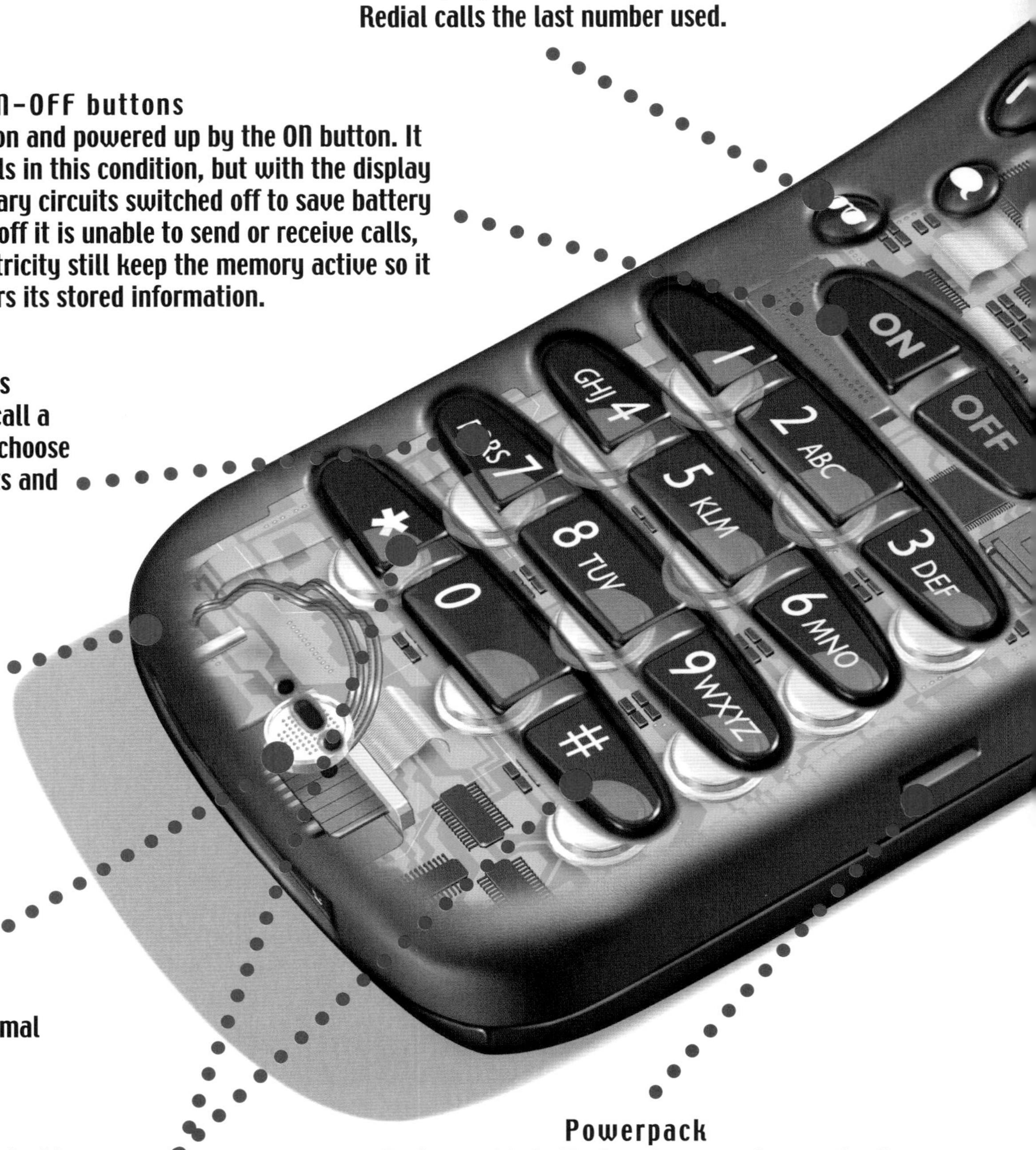

Recall and redial
Recall brings names, phone numbers, addresses and notes from the memory and displays them on the screen. Redial calls the last number used.

ON-OFF buttons
The mobile is switched on and powered up by the ON button. It can receive incoming calls in this condition, but with the display light and other unnecessary circuits switched off to save battery power. When switched off it is unable to send or receive calls, but tiny amounts of electricity still keep the memory active so it remembers its stored information.

Number (digit) buttons
These buttons are pressed to call a certain telephone number or to choose numbered options from the lists and menus on the screen.

Case
The mobile phone is protected inside a strong plastic case moulded to fit easily in the hand. It may have another cover over the top to cushion the phone from knocks, protect it from splashes and lessen the risk of the phone being switched on or buttons pressed by accident.

Mouthpiece
This is a miniature simplified microphone, the same as in a normal telephone handset.

Hash and star buttons
The hash (#) and star (*) are used for automated calls when communicating with a recorded voice and computer, where a number button might cause confusion. For example, the hash button may be pressed to show the end of a sequence of digits, such as a credit card number.

Powerpack
Rechargeable batteries give many hours of call time and more than a week of standby time (switched on and able to receive calls). They supply only a few volts of electricity. They are recharged by plugging the phone into its power supply recharger which is connected to the mains.

MORE AND MORE MOBILES

No gadget in history has sold so well and advanced so fast as the mobile phone. In 1998 Finland became the first country to have more mobile phones than fixed phones. By the year 2000 in many countries, more people had mobile phones than those who did not. Some mobiles can be linked to the Internet and have miniature screens on them for truly mobile global communications.

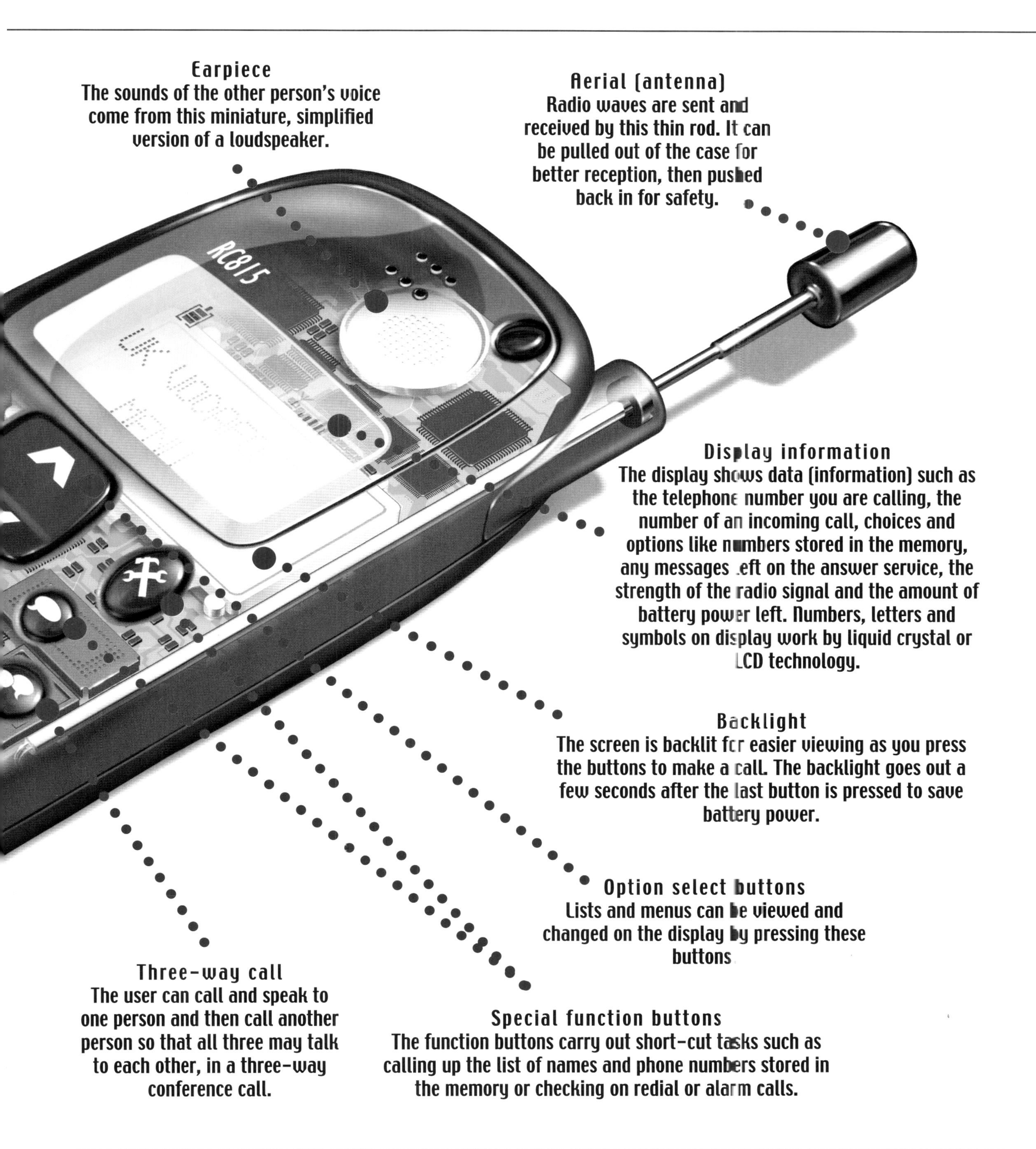

HOW MOBILES WORK

A mobile phone is really a low-power radio transmitter and receiver. When switched on it sends out radio signals that are detected by nearby cellular transmitter-receivers. Each of these sends and receives by radio over a local area or 'cell'. Several receivers may send their identity signals back to the phone. The phone then selects the most suitable receiver and establishes connection through it to the network.

The size of a cell varies but is usually a few kilometres across. Cities where more people are packed together have small cells, because each cell can cope with only a limited number of calls. Also tall buildings or hills might disrupt signals and cause dead spots.

If you use a mobile on the move, it detects the fading signal as it moves farther away from the cell's transmitter-receiver. As soon as possible it automatically switches to the stronger signal in the next cell along.

PERSONAL STEREO

Audio mini-cassette
The cassette is a small case of magnetic tape used for sound only (audio). It has two spools. When the tape play direction reverses, the supply spool becomes the take-up spool.

Playback head
This detects the varying pattern of magnetic patches on the tape as it slides past and converts them into a similar pattern of electrical signals for the earpieces.

Tape guide
Revolving pulleys of smooth plastic guide the tape around corners.

Play button
This large button switches on the tape play motor and works a lever that presses the pinch wheel against the motor capstan to make the tape move along.

Tape reverse switch
The direction of the tape drive motor and capstan can be reversed so that the tape slides in the opposite direction, when the supply spool becomes the take-up spool. This means you do not have to take out the cassette and turn it over to play the other side.

Tape select
Various types of tapes have different particles in the magnetic coating. For better sound quality, these are usually ferric or Fe (iron), CrO_2 (chromium dioxide) or metal (a combination of various magnetic metals).

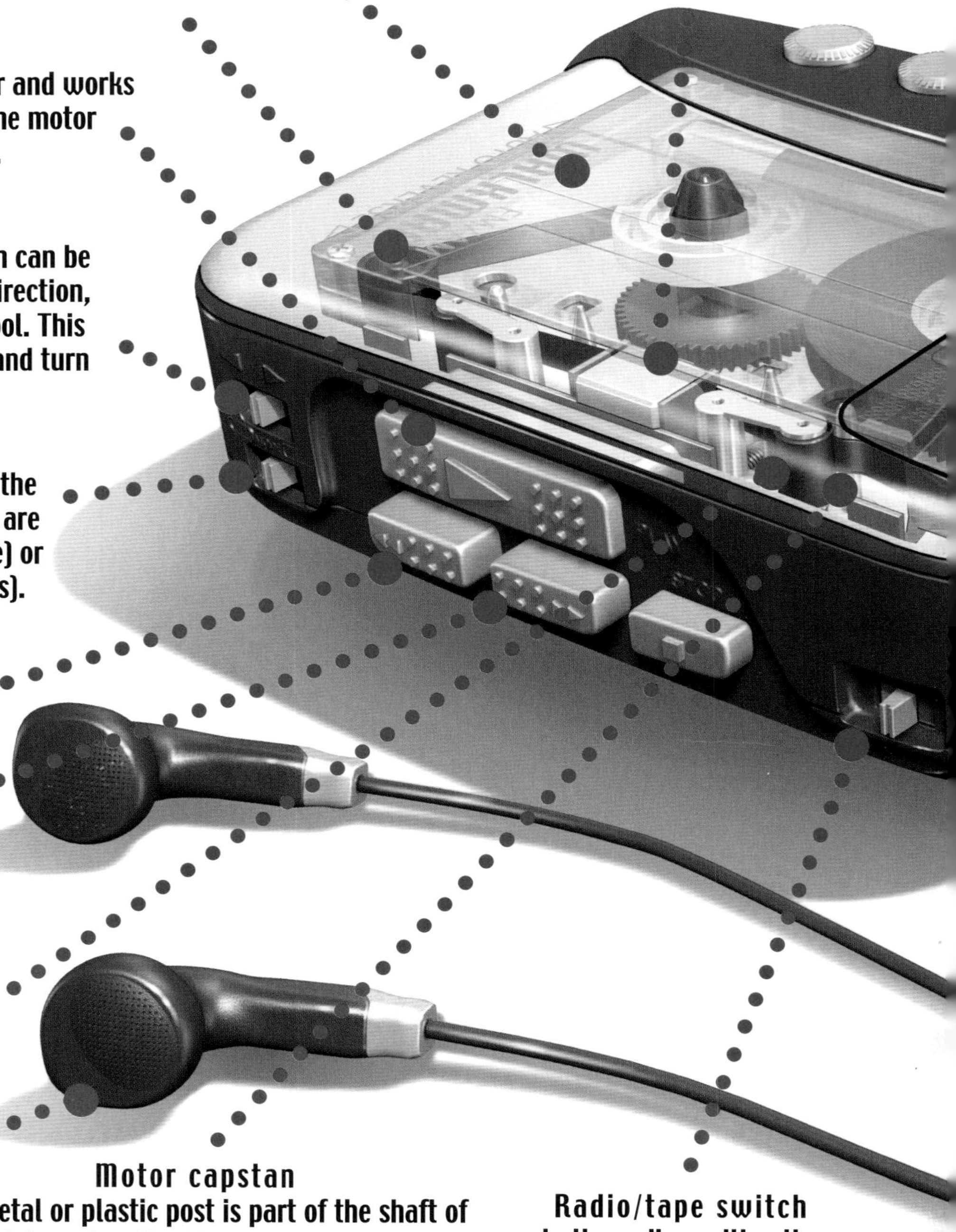

Fast rewind button
RW (FR or REW) makes the motor turn the supply tape spool at high speed to wind back the tape.

Fast forward button
FF (FWD) makes the motor turn the take-up tape spool at high speed to wind on the tape.

Pinch wheel
The rubber pinch wheel pushes or pinches the tape against the motor capstan when the play button is pressed, to make the tape move along.

Earpiece
This is an in-the-ear design that fits snugly into the middle part of the ear. The two earpieces are not identical. The plastic cases are shaped differently and marked L and R for left and right ears.

Motor capstan
This metal or plastic post is part of the shaft of the electric motor. It whizzes around and makes the tape, pressed against it by the pinch wheel, move along at a constant speed – no matter how much of the tape is on the take-up spool.

Radio/tape switch
In the radio position the electricity supply to the tape motors and playback head circuits is switched off.

CASSETTE TAPE

Mini-cassette audio tape is about 4 millimetres (one-twelfth of an inch) wide and some 260 metres (715 feet) long for a playing time of 90 minutes (C90). It is made of a flexible plastic strip coated with a layer of tiny magnetic particles, and on top of this is another layer for protection and smooth running past the playback head.

INSIDE THE EAR

Headphones or earpieces work in a similar way to loudspeakers. In the 1970s earpieces became much smaller while still giving clear, loud sounds, especially to low or bass notes. This improvement was due to new and very powerful combinations of magnetic materials, such as samarium-cobalt. There are various earpiece designs:

- In-the-ear as shown here.
- Around-the-ear with a flexible plastic loop that hooks around the back of the ear flap.
- Side-entry where the earpiece is shaped like a button but fits sideways into the ear leaving an air gap around it. This type is worn on a headband.
- Headphones also have a headband over the top of the head. A foam-edged, cup-shaped cushion fits over the whole ear to help cut out sounds from the surroundings.
- Some headphones have fluid-filled cushions that mould themselves exactly to the shape of the person's ear.

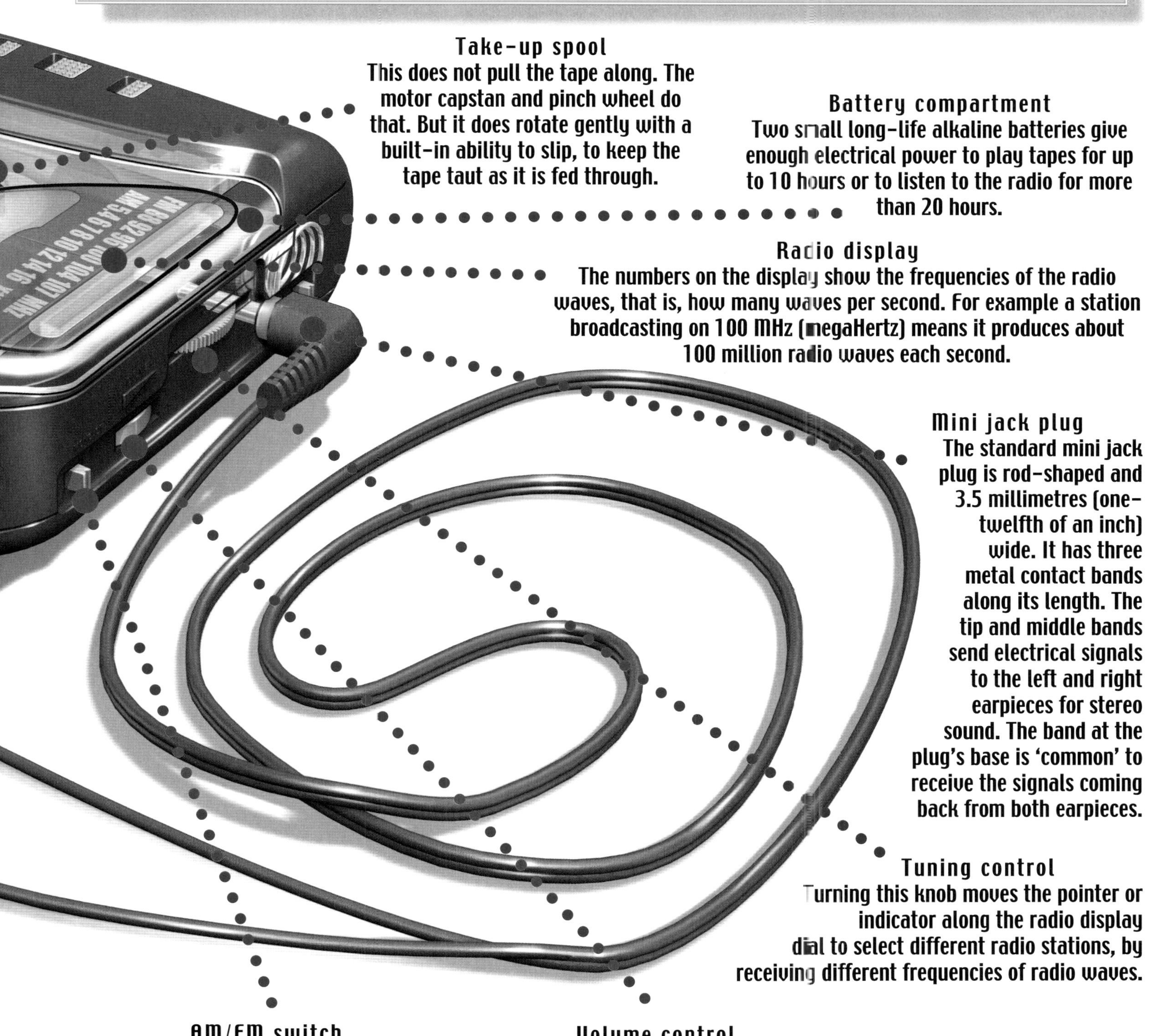

SYNTHESIZER

Built-in speaker
The sounds generated by the synthesizer can be played through its own small stereo loudspeakers, with left and right channels, especially when putting sounds together to check how they are coming along. The signals are sent to a bigger and more powerful sound system when performing in front of many people.

Sampler effect
External sounds can be recorded in the digital memory for sampling, changing or manipulation later. A snatch or sample of recorded sound can be altered by changing it from a low to high pitch, by making it faster or slower or by filtering out some of the pitches or frequencies.

Mode switch
The synthesizer can be used to deal with and manipulate individual sounds or groups of sounds, one after the other, and then combine together or arrange all of the individual sounds and groups into one musical piece.

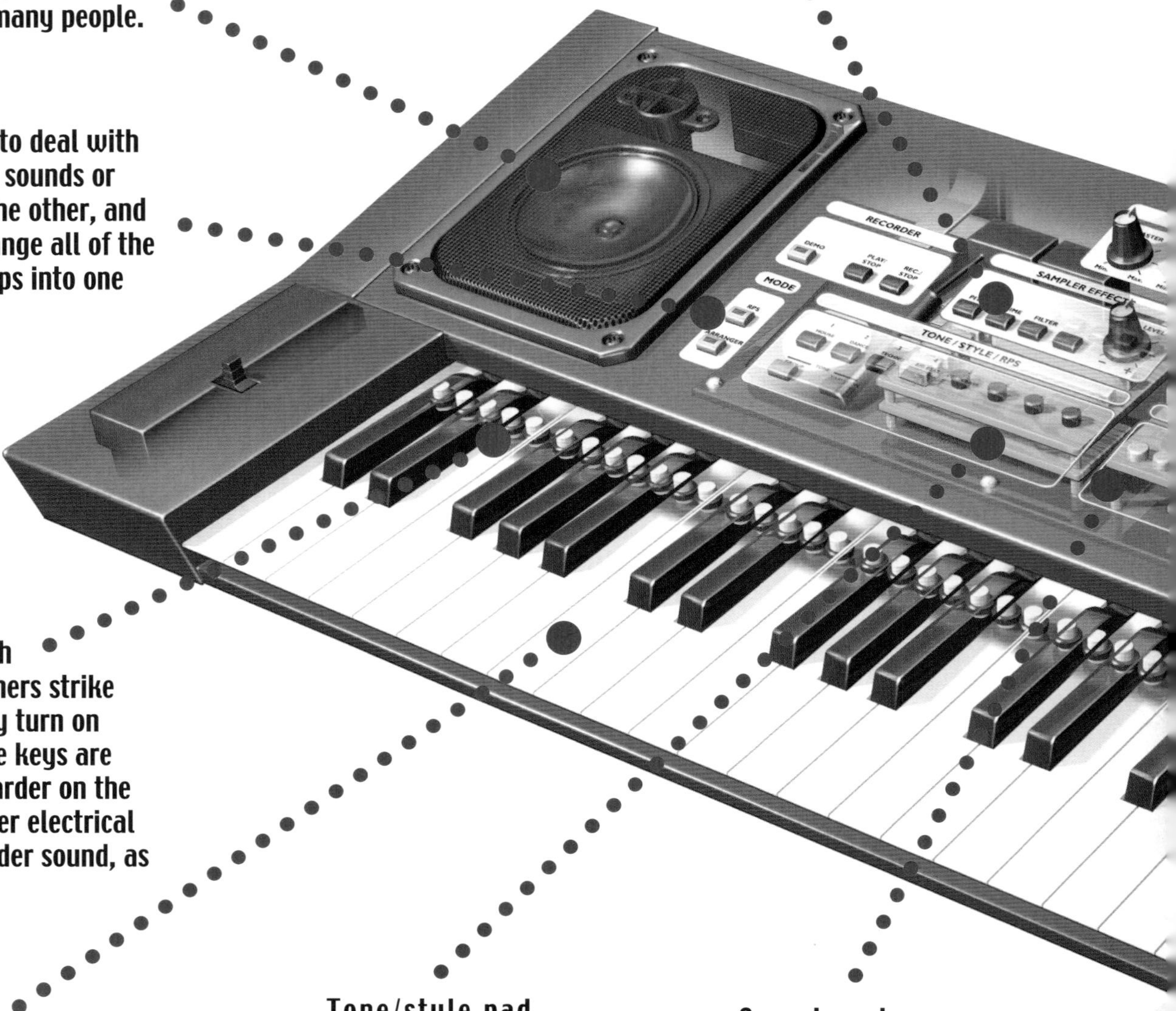

Pressure switch
The keys don't make hammers strike strings as in a piano. They turn on electrical switches. But the keys are touch-sensitive. Pressing harder on the key makes it produce stronger electrical signals which end up as a louder sound, as on a real piano.

Keyboard
The keyboard notes are laid out in the traditional manner of a piano or organ. The white notes are A, B, C and so on through to F, and then A, B, C and so on again. This is the traditional 'doe-ray-mee' musical scale. The black keys are in-between notes called sharps or flats. The note shown here is C.

Tone/style pad
The synthesizer has various types and styles of music already built into its memory, such as different drum rhythms for rock, house, hip-hop, techno, reggae and so on. These can be used unaltered and 'straight' or changed in the manipulator.

Sampler player
This plays or slots the different samples of sound from the memory into the whole arranged piece of music.

SAMPLING

A sample is a short snatch or piece of sound, taken out or isolated from another sound recording. It may be a single drum beat, a few seconds of massed violins, a word or two in a song or the screaming wail of an electric guitar. In the form of electrical signals it can then be altered and added into another recording.

MUSIC FROM NOWHERE

Acoustic instruments such as drums, trumpets and violins make their sounds in a physical way. They have fast to-and-fro vibrations that cause sound waves in the air. Electronic instruments such as the synthesizer don't begin with sound waves. They make up different patterns of electrical signals which are then put together or synthesized and converted into sound waves by loudspeakers or headphones.

Real sound waves can be altered or manipulated slightly. A cup-like mute placed over the end of a trumpet makes its notes sound thin and weak. But electrical signals can be manipulated in many more different ways. They can be cut up and pasted together, made faster or slower, bigger or smaller, and with smoother or sharper wave shapes. You can see what you are doing as the signals are shown as waves, spikes or bars on a display.

Arpeggio
An arpeggio is a set of notes that go together to make up a chord, but which are played rapidly one after the other instead of all together. (It's like picking out the strings of a guitar quickly one after the other rather than strumming all of them together.)

Effects
Various effects such as echoes, wah-wah or a flanger that gives a 'whooshing' sensation, can be added to the basic sounds.

Manipulator
Different notes or frequencies of sound can be isolated and changed by making them louder or softer, longer or shorter, higher or lower, continuous or stuttering and so on.

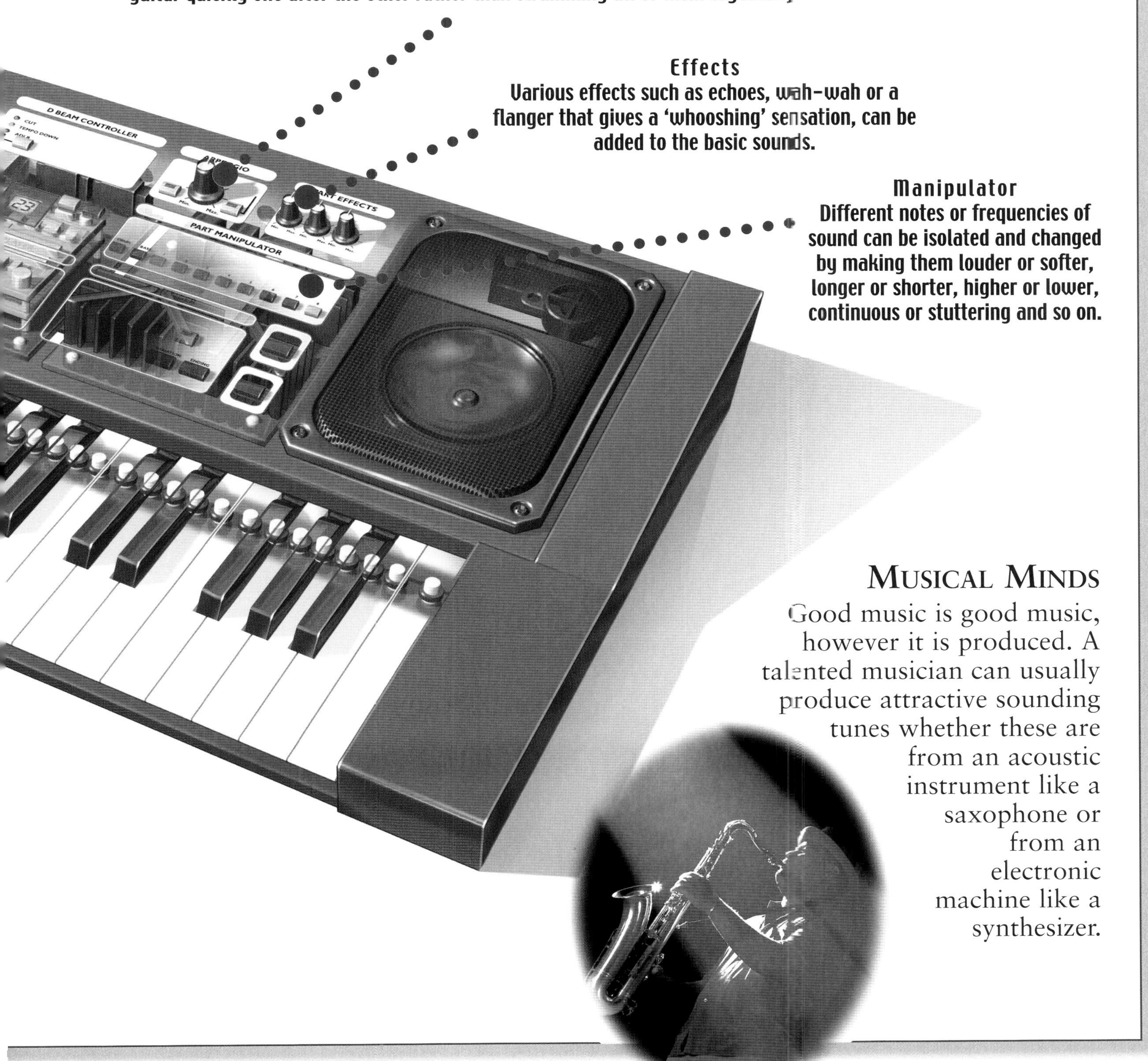

MUSICAL MINDS

Good music is good music, however it is produced. A talented musician can usually produce attractive sounding tunes whether these are from an acoustic instrument like a saxophone or from an electronic machine like a synthesizer.

MICROWAVE OVEN

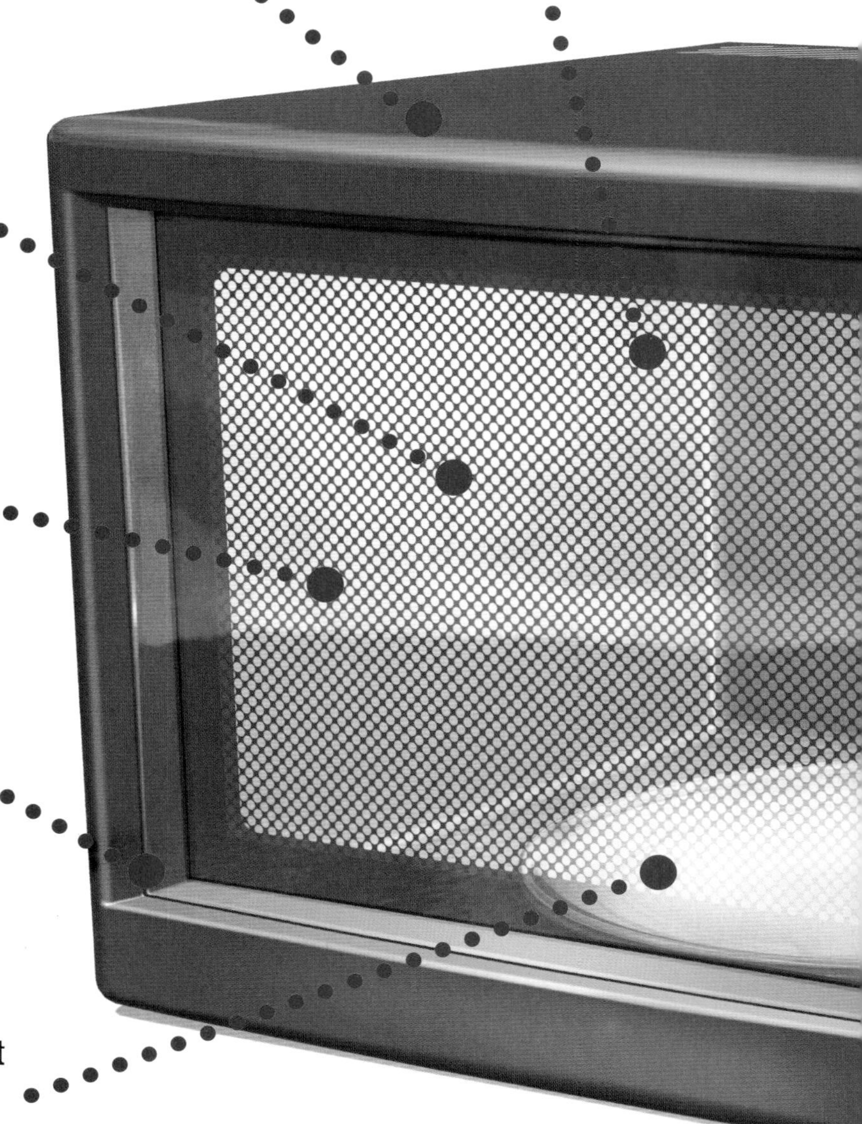

Microwave-proof case
The metal casing prevents microwaves from escaping and possibly causing harm to people or animals near by.

Internal light
The light comes on automatically, both to show that the microwave oven is working and so that you can see the cooking food inside.

Lining
The lining of the oven reflects microwaves so that they bounce about inside and their energy is used, and so that they do not leak through the walls and cause problems outside.

Protective grill door
The grill allows you to see what is happening inside the oven, to check whether the food is cooked, but it does not let microwaves out.

Door seal
The most likely place for microwaves to escape is around the door seal when this gets worn, loose or broken. Safety checks involve looking carefully at the condition of the seal. A microwave meter held nearby can detect if there is any leakage.

Revolving platter
The food turns round on this large plate so that it cooks more evenly and thoroughly. In some versions the platter stops and revolves in the opposite direction after a certain amount of time.

WHAT ARE MICROWAVES?

Microwaves are a form of what is known as EM (electromagnetic) energy. They are invisible up-and-down waves of both magnetism and electricity. There is a whole range of these waves, known as the EM spectrum. The longest, with individual waves many metres or even kilometres long, are called radio waves. Microwaves are each about 1–100 centimetres (half an inch to 39 inches) long.

Much, much shorter, with waves only millionths of a metre long, are visible light rays. These are the only electromagnetic waves we can see. Next shortest are ultraviolet waves and then X-rays and gamma rays. All these waves travel at the speed of light, about 300,000 kilometres (186,000 miles) per second.

HOW MICROWAVES HEAT

Microwaves work mainly by agitating or shaking the molecules of water within the food. A molecule that shakes or vibrates more has more heat energy, that is, it gets hotter. The heat energy is transferred from each water molecule to the other molecules around it. The food cooks inside, rather than from the outside inwards as in a normal oven. The process also continues for a time after the microwaves are switched off. So food from a microwave oven is left to 'stand' for a time afterwards to finish cooking.

Paddles
Some microwave ovens have revolving paddles, like a fan in the roof. These help to scatter the microwaves around inside the oven for more even, thorough cooking.

Waveguide
Microwaves made by the magnetron are led along the hollow waveguide and into the general oven compartment.

Magnetron
This works in a similar way to a TV 'tube' (cathode ray tube). A high-voltage electric current heats a part called a cathode. This gives off energy, which is converted into microwaves. The waves are made at the rate of about 2,500 million every second.

Step-up transformer
The mains electricity is increased in voltage for the magnetron.

Control buttons
The buttons program the cooking time, cooking power and other information for the oven. Preset buttons make it easier to cook fairly standard items such as a chicken.

Step-down transformer
The mains electricity is reduced in voltage for the electronic control circuits.

Pause button
The cooking can be paused for a short period by stopping the magnetron and revolving platter. Information such as the cooking time and power are kept in the memory for when cooking resumes.

Door lock button
The door is locked shut and can't be opened while the oven is working so that microwaves cannot escape.

Start button
This switches on the magnetron, timing and power circuits, oven light and revolving platter.

POWER DRILL

Reverse switch
Normally a twist drill rotates clockwise. This switch makes it turn the other way, anti-clockwise. It can be useful when the twist drill has 'screwed' itself rapidly into a soft substance and can't be pulled out easily.

Reduction gears
At full speed the motor spins far too fast to be useful for turning a twist drill. The reduction gears slow down the speed of rotation, and at the same time, by the principle of mechanics, make the turning force more powerful.

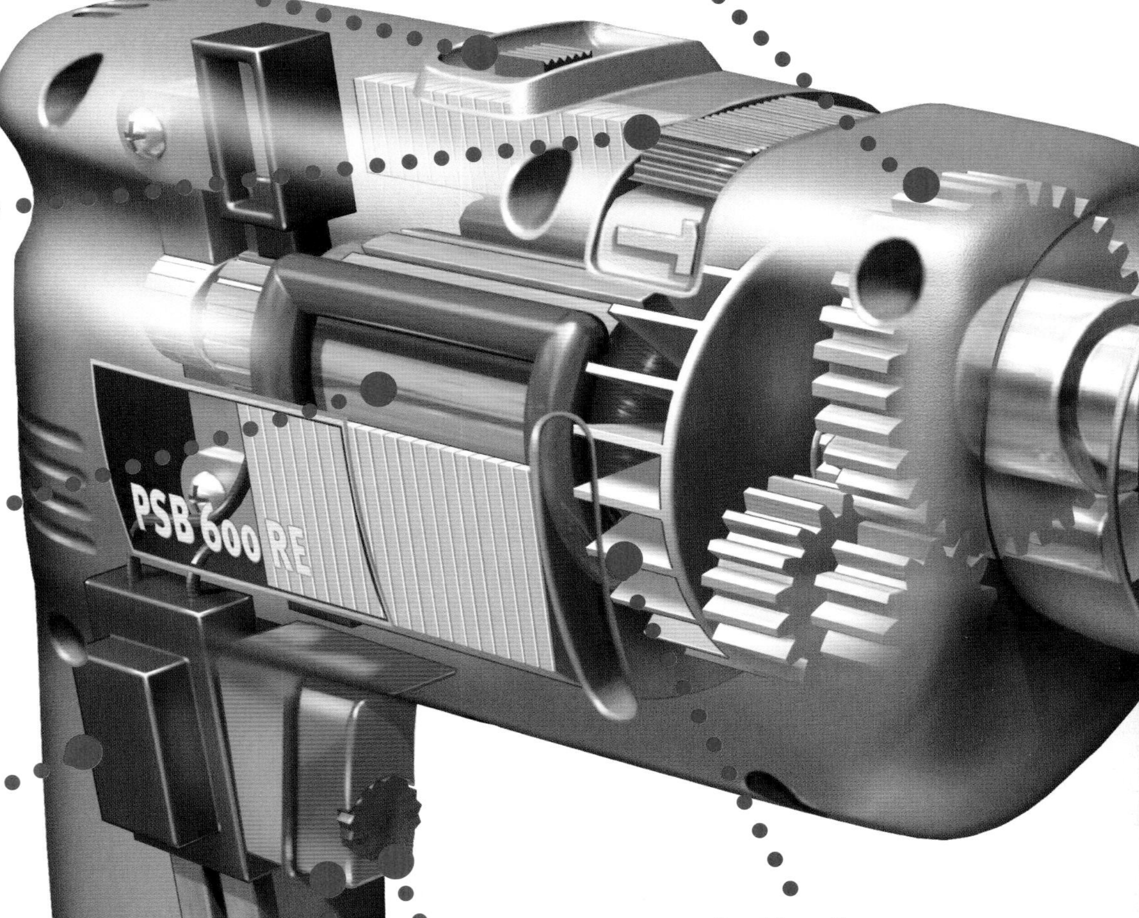

Hammer switch
In the hammer position the drill bit not only turns around but also punches forwards many times each second. It is used for drilling into very hard substances, such as rock, mortar and concrete.

Electric motor
The powerful electric motor has many sets of coils or windings so it rotates smoothly.

Speed control circuit
These circuits feed the electric current controlled by the variable speed dial and trigger up to the electric motor.

Cooling fan
Whirling fan blades spin with the motor to push air past it so that it does not overheat. They also blow loose material from the hole away from the motor so that it does not clog.

Handle grip
This is the main handle for holding and gripping the tool. Pushing it forwards provides the force to drive the drill bit into the object. However, too much force will cause the drill bit to overheat or stick, or the motor to burn out. The pistol grip handle at the front of the drill steadies and positions the front of the drill for two-handed operations, to make sure the drill tip does not slip sideways on a hard, shiny surface and begin a hole in the wrong place.

Variable speed dial
The knob is turned to control the maximum speed of the drill, that is, the fastest rate it turns when the trigger is pushed in fully.

Variable speed trigger
The more the trigger is pushed in, the faster the drill bit rotates, up to a maximum speed set by the variable speed dial.

More Power

A modern workshop is packed with electrical power tools, including circular saws, jigsaws with narrow blades that go up and down very fast, orbital sanders, belt sanders and grinders with rotating discs.

Depth gauge
This sliding rod can be pulled forwards by a measured amount and then secured in position with a screw. As you drill into an object the end of the rod moves towards it. When the end of the rod touches the surface of the object the hole is the correct depth.

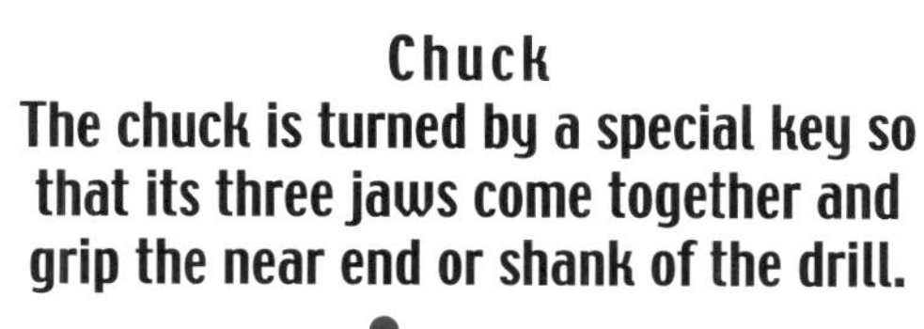

Chuck
The chuck is turned by a special key so that its three jaws come together and grip the near end or shank of the drill.

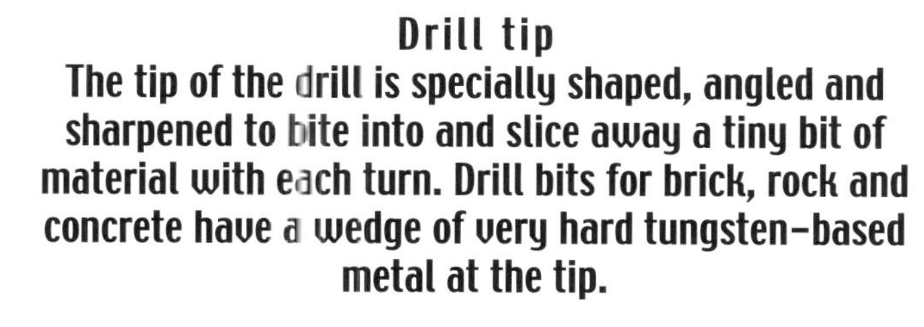

Drill tip
The tip of the drill is specially shaped, angled and sharpened to bite into and slice away a tiny bit of material with each turn. Drill bits for brick, rock and concrete have a wedge of very hard tungsten-based metal at the tip.

Drill bit
The drill has helical (corkscrew-like) slots along its sides. These gather the loose material that the drill bit has cut away and push it back out of the hole so it does not collect and clog.

GEARING UP

Many machines and gadgets use gears, from power drills and concrete mixers to bicycles and racing cars. There are two main features of gearing. First is turning rate, usually measured in revolutions per minute or second. If two gear wheels have same number of same-sized teeth, one will drive the other at the same speed. If one is large with twice as many teeth as the other, the larger one will make the smaller one turn at twice the speed. So gears can be used to change the speed of rotation for different tasks. However there is a price to pay...

GEARING DOWN

The second feature of gearing is turning power, known as torque. In the above example, when the large gear wheel drives the small one it will make the small one spin twice as fast – but with only half the turning force or torque of the large one. This is because, in mechanics, you cannot get something for nothing. In the power drill shown here, the reduction gears mean that the motor may spin 20 times faster than the drill bit. But this gives the drill bit much greater torque to bore into an object.

GO-PED

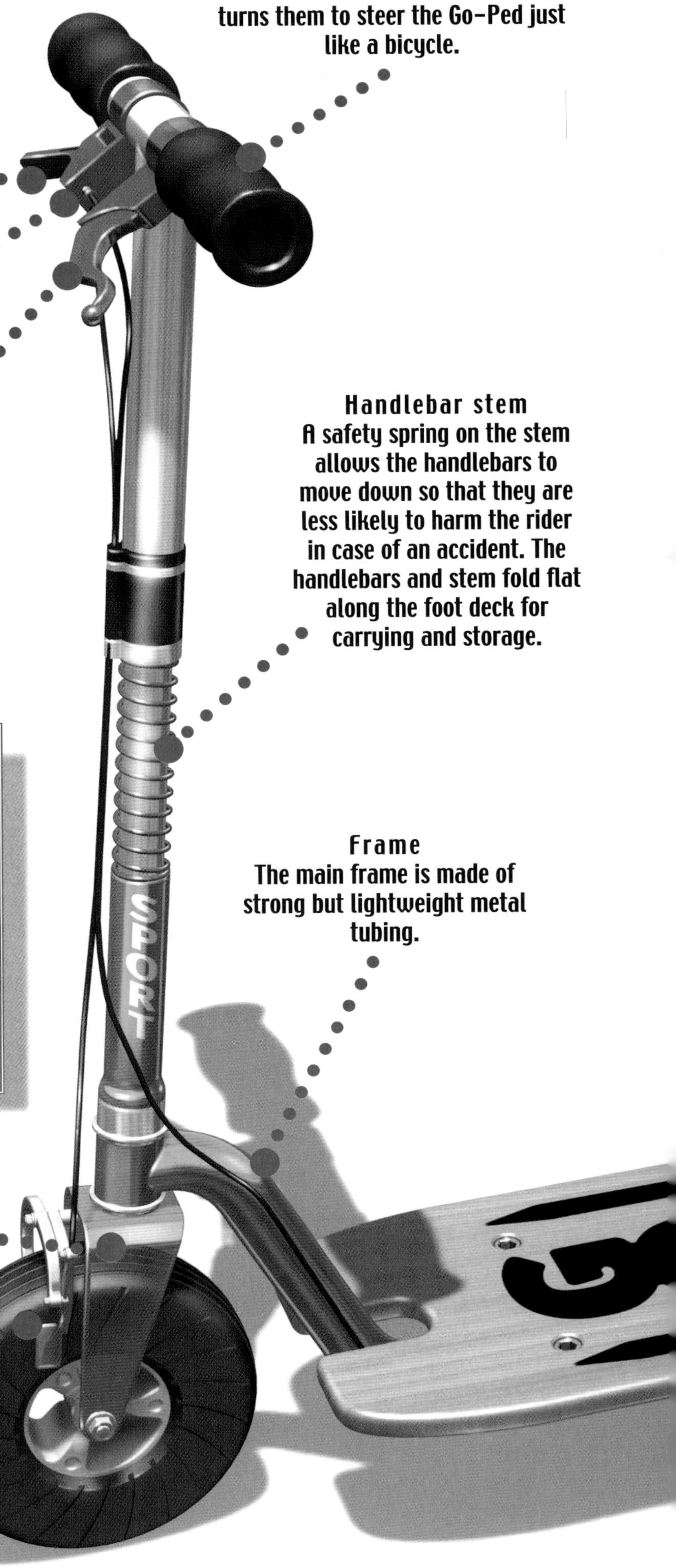

Handlebars
The rider holds both handlebars and turns them to steer the Go-Ped just like a bicycle.

Throttle trigger
The trigger is linked to the engine throttle by a cable. The throttle supplies more fuel and air to the engine to increase its speed and so make the vehicle go faster, up to 32 kph (20 mph).

Engine kill
An easily accessible switch cuts off and stops the engine in case of problems or an emergency.

Handlebar stem
A safety spring on the stem allows the handlebars to move down so that they are less likely to harm the rider in case of an accident. The handlebars and stem fold flat along the foot deck for carrying and storage.

Brake lever
Pulling on the lever works the front caliper brakes by a long cable, as on a bicycle.

SPECIAL ENGINE
The two-stroke petrol engine is similar to those used in some power tools, and also in certain off-road or track motorcycles. In some Go-Peds it drives the rear tyre via a roller. In others it is linked by a transmission unit that only makes the rear wheel turn as the engine gains speed and power. This allows the vehicle to stay still with the engine running.

Frame
The main frame is made of strong but lightweight metal tubing.

Front fork
The fork holds the front wheel and tyre, which turn to one side or the other and steer the vehicle.

Brake
Caliper brakes make the brake blocks press against the tyre to slow down the vehicle.

Wheel and tyre
The tyre is not air-filled (pneumatic) but solid natural rubber. It cannot suffer punctures, yet it still smoothes out lumps and bumps in the road.

PPT

Personal powered transport is a very busy area for engineers and inventors. The small vehicles use fewer raw materials and much less fuel than a car, reducing demand for natural resources and cutting pollution.

- The Go-Ped 'motorized skateboard' is small, convenient and lightweight, and can be transported easily when not in use. It carries up to 180 kilograms (almost 400 pounds) so it can be used for shopping. However, it is not suited to wet and slippery surfaces.
- Similar two-wheeled scooter or cycle-type designs driven by electric motors are also being developed. They carry rechargeable powerpacks of batteries that are plugged into the mains electricity overnight.
- The mini-bubble car has three wheels like those on a tricycle and is powered by an engine. The wrap-around clear plastic bubble protects the driver from rain and danger.

Up and Away

Whenever a new vehicle or craft is invented, people begin to hold races and competitions and to test each other's skills. Motorcycles soon evolved into special 'dirt bikes' on which riders negotiate mud, hills, water jumps and fallen logs.

Fuel tank
The tank holds the usual mixture of petrol and two-stroke oil designed for two-stroke petrol engines.

Foot deck
The rider stands and balances on the deck as the vehicle moves along. He or she leans slightly to the side to go around curves, but not so much as on a motorcycle because the Go-Ped's wheels are so much smaller.

Engine
The two-stroke petrol engine drives the rear wheel directly. Whenever it is running the rear wheel turns.

Centre stand
Levered on to this stand the Go-Ped stays upright and the rear wheel is off the ground, for starting or for staying still with the engine running and the rear wheel turning.

Pull start
With the rear wheel off the ground, the start cord is pulled out sharply to turn over the engine and get it working. Once the engine has been warmed up, it can be started again after being stopped by 'scooting' the Go-Ped along.

SCUBA

Tank
Air or a special mixture of breathing gases is pumped into here. It's at a very high pressure, so a large volume becomes extremely squeezed or compressed into a small space.

Water pressure
The surrounding water presses on the high-pressure diaphragm to make the valve open when necessary and to keep up the intermediate pressure in the first stage regulator chamber and the air hose.

On-Off valve
This tap seals or closes the tank so air cannot come out into the first stage regulator. It's used to turn the tank 'off' when not in use and also when refilling it.

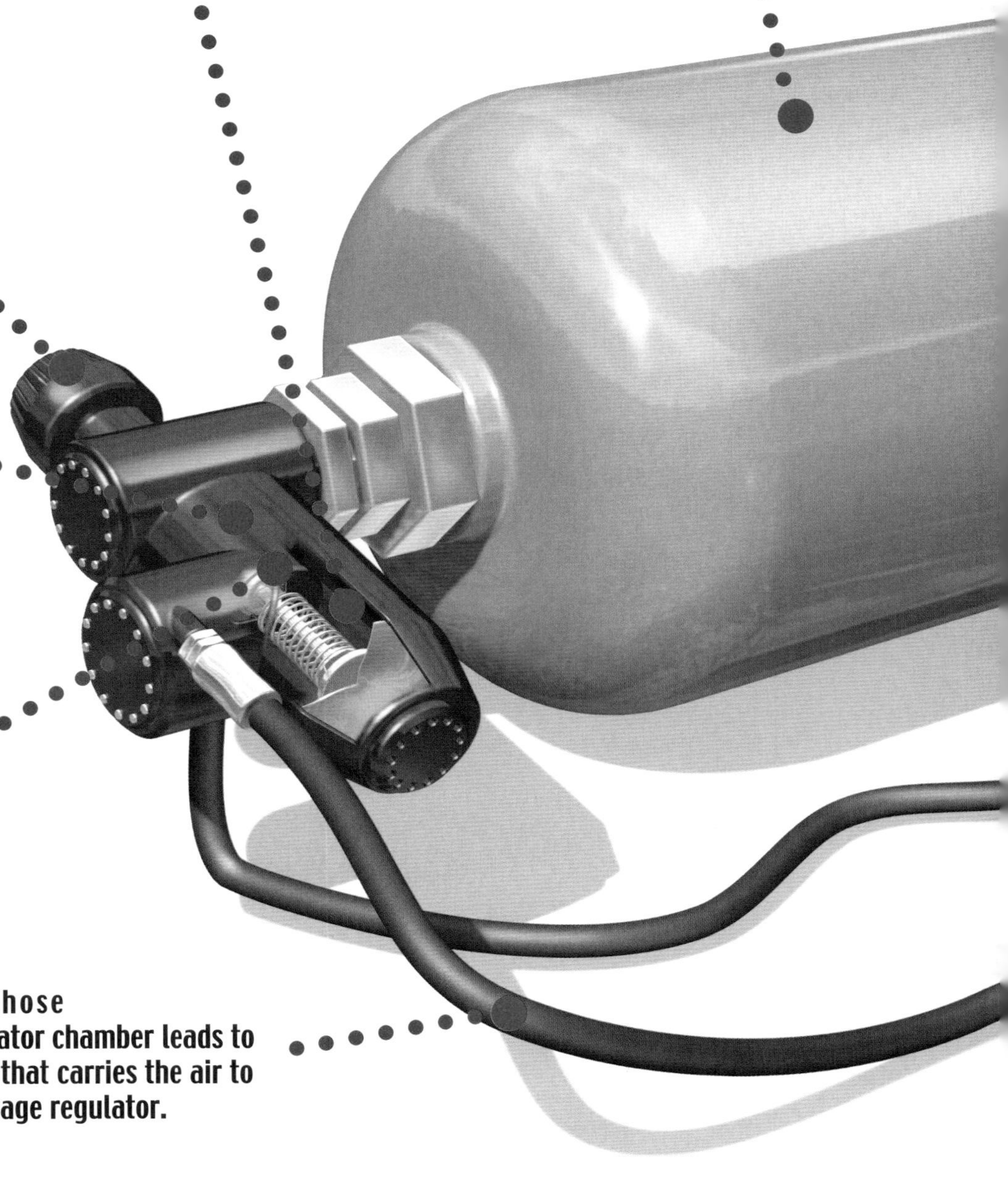

First stage regulator
The first regulator reduces the very high pressure of the air in the tank to an in-between or intermediate pressure in the air hose, about 80-150 pounds per square inch.

Valve
The valve keeps the high-pressure air in the tank unless the pressure in the air hose drops, then it lets some air from the tank into the first stage regulator chamber and hose.

Air hose
The first stage regulator chamber leads to the flexible air hose that carries the air to the second stage regulator.

OUT OF BREATH

There are many ways of seeing the underwater world, watching fish swim, admiring the incredible variety and colour of life on the coral reef or even hunting for shipwrecks and buried treasure. Most forms of diving require some equipment. But in free diving the diver has no gadgets, equipment or artificial aids at all. With plenty of care, practise and expert help on standby, some divers can stay under for more than 20 minutes or descend below 150 metres. But such feats are extremely specialized and very dangerous. Most people struggle to stay under for more than a minute or descend to below about 4–5 metres.

WHAT IS SCUBA?

The letters stand for Self-Contained Underwater Breathing Apparatus. It's a piece of equipment that lets you swim freely underwater for long periods of time, without having to come up for air. Before scuba gear, divers had to hold their breath or they were attached by tubes or hoses which carried air down to them from the surface. They also had to undergo hours of special training and be physically fit and healthy.

Scuba gear, after a period of training, can be used by almost anyone. It has opened up the exciting underwater world to millions of people. The early and well-known type of scuba called the aqua lung appeared in the early 1940s. It was developed by Emil Gagnan and the famous French diver, film-maker, writer, conservationist and ocean expert Jacques-Yves Cousteau.

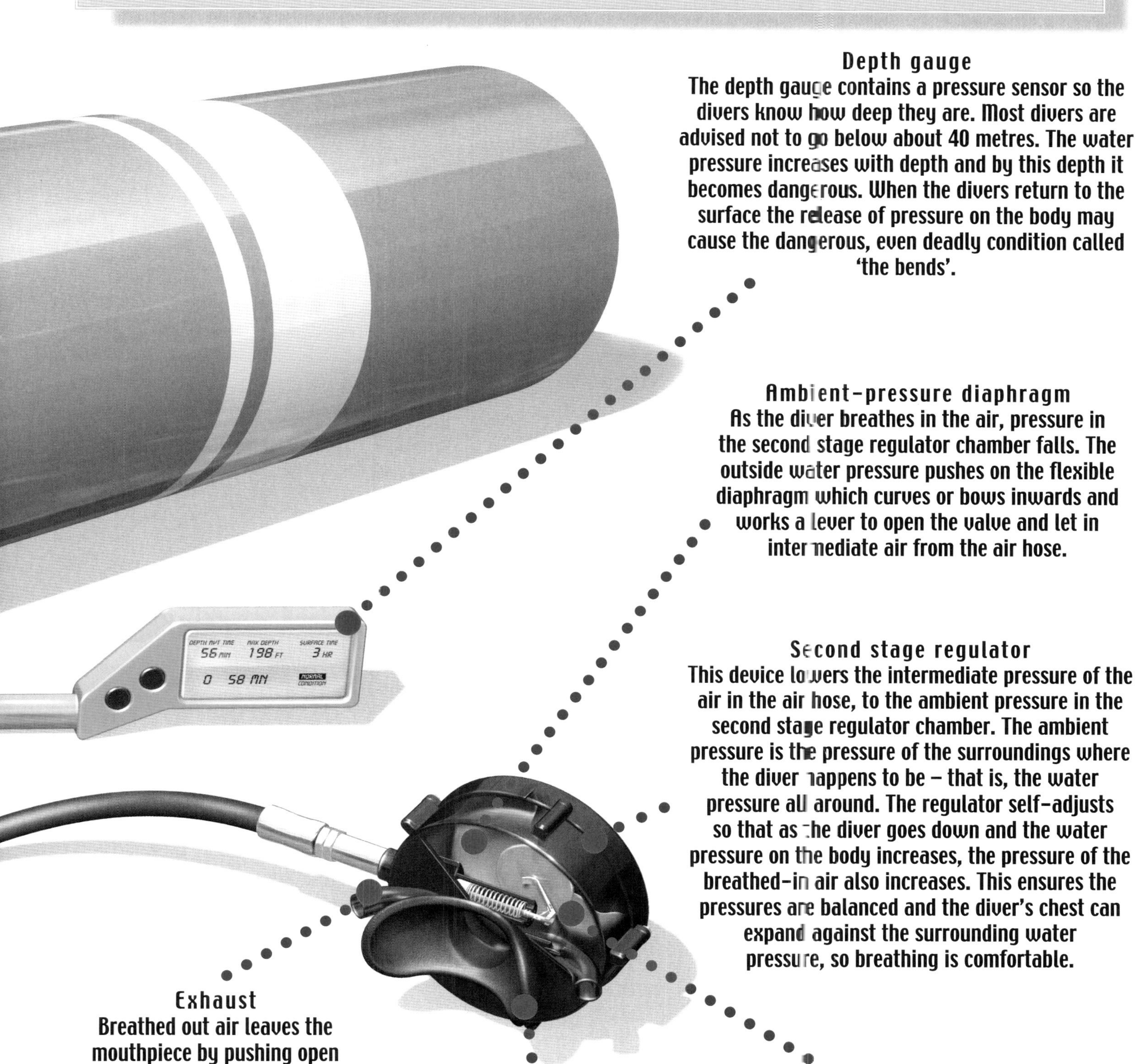

Depth gauge
The depth gauge contains a pressure sensor so the divers know how deep they are. Most divers are advised not to go below about 40 metres. The water pressure increases with depth and by this depth it becomes dangerous. When the divers return to the surface the release of pressure on the body may cause the dangerous, even deadly condition called 'the bends'.

Ambient-pressure diaphragm
As the diver breathes in the air, pressure in the second stage regulator chamber falls. The outside water pressure pushes on the flexible diaphragm which curves or bows inwards and works a lever to open the valve and let in intermediate air from the air hose.

Second stage regulator
This device lowers the intermediate pressure of the air in the air hose, to the ambient pressure in the second stage regulator chamber. The ambient pressure is the pressure of the surroundings where the diver happens to be – that is, the water pressure all around. The regulator self-adjusts so that as the diver goes down and the water pressure on the body increases, the pressure of the breathed-in air also increases. This ensures the pressures are balanced and the diver's chest can expand against the surrounding water pressure, so breathing is comfortable.

Exhaust
Breathed out air leaves the mouthpiece by pushing open flap-like valves into the exhaust manifolds, and then out into the water. It produces a stream of bubbles with each breath.

Mouthpiece
Air flows from the second stage regulator chamber through the mouthpiece, into the diver's mouth and own breathing system.

Valve
The valve opens when worked by the ambient-pressure diaphragm and lever, to let air from the air hose pass into the second stage regulator chamber. This air can then be breathed in.

HOLOGRAM

Holographic image
The holographic image recorded on the film does not look like an ordinary photographic image, which is a realistic picture of the object with dark and light areas of different colours. The holographic image is recorded as an interference pattern or interferogram.

Coherent light waves
Every light wave from a laser has the same length. (In ordinary light the waves have different lengths, which give them different colours.) Also all the waves are in step or in phase so they rise and fall together, with their peaks lined up. (In ordinary light the waves are not in step or in phase and rise and fall at random.)

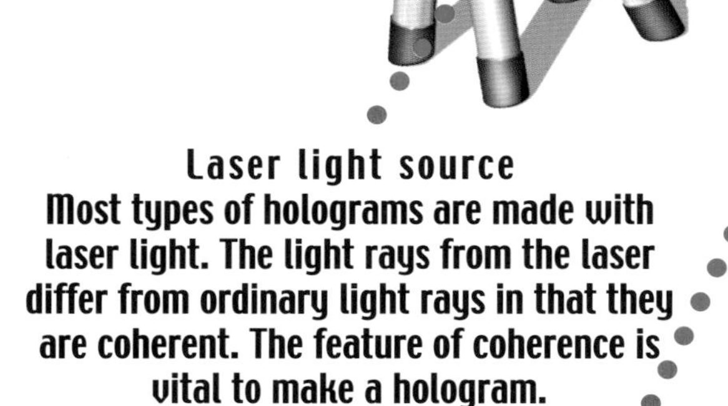

Laser light source
Most types of holograms are made with laser light. The light rays from the laser differ from ordinary light rays in that they are coherent. The feature of coherence is vital to make a hologram.

Beam splitter
This focuses and splits or separates the laser beam into two parts, the object beam and reference beam.

Reference beam
The reference part of the original laser light beam shines directly on to the photographic film where the holographic picture or image is recorded.

Viewing the Hologram
To view a holographic image, light must shine on it in a certain way. There are two main kinds of holograms with different ways of doing this. In a transmission hologram the same type of laser light used in the original reference beam is shone on to the image to illuminate it. A reflection hologram uses ordinary daylight which has been altered or filtered to illuminate it. The reflection hologram is more convenient to look at since you don't need to shine a laser beam on it. But it usually gives a smaller, less clear image.

Reflected object beam
The object beam bounces or reflects off the object being photographed and then shines onto the photographic film.

WHAT ARE HOLOGRAMS USED FOR?
Holograms have many different uses. They can be found on small pictures on identity cards, licences, credit-cash cards, security passes and similar personal documents. Architects and planners may use them for 3-D plans of the insides of big buildings, underground railway networks or the maze of pipes, drains, tunnels and wires under a city. Scientists might have 3-D holographic maps of the atoms in a tiny molecule. Holograms are also used as 3-D memory in computers. And they are often used for publicity stunts, advertising, exhibitions and works of art in their own right.

DOTS AND CIRCLES

The holographic image recorded on photographic film is not a realistic picture or view like an ordinary photograph. If you could see a microscopic view it would have millions of dark spots surrounded by alternating dark and light curved lines, like ripples on a pond when a stone is thrown in. This is an interferogram. Imagine that as two light rays hit the same spot on the film they are in phase with their wave peaks lined up. This forms a light area. But in other places two light rays are out of phase. For example one wave is at its high point or peak and the other is at its low point or trough. So the waves 'interfere' and cancel each other out to form a dark area. A holographic image is this pattern of light wave interference – an interferogram. To create a normal life-like picture it must be viewed in a special way.

Photographic film
Like ordinary film for a normal camera, this has billions of spots of light-sensitive chemicals in it. They change when the film is exposed, that is, when the object and reference laser beams shine on to it. The changed chemicals record the pattern of laser light waves which hit it to make up the holographic image.

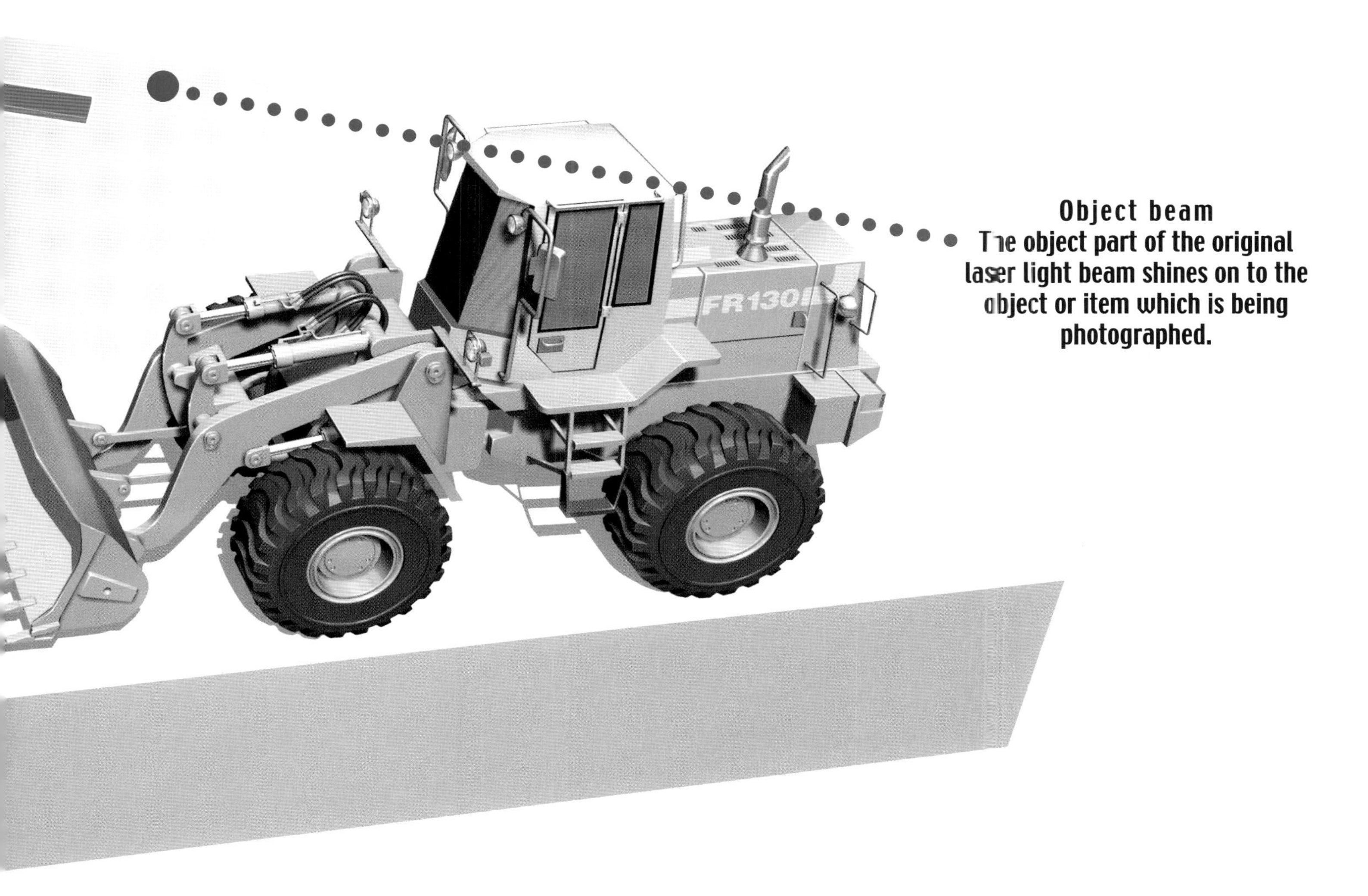

Object beam
The object part of the original laser light beam shines on to the object or item which is being photographed.

HOLOGRAMS ARE 3-D PICTURES

Normal photographs and pictures are two-dimensional, 2-D. They have width and height. But they do not have depth. You can see items at different distances, but you cannot look around them to see what is behind. Only the parts of the scene directly facing the camera are in the picture. A hologram (which means 'whole picture') is three-dimensional, 3-D. It shows all parts of the scene, including the sides and back of objects and what is behind them. If you move to the side you can see around objects and look at things that were 'hidden' behind them. This 3-D quality makes holograms very life-like and sometimes startling and eerie.

VIDEO CASSETTE RECORDER (VCR)

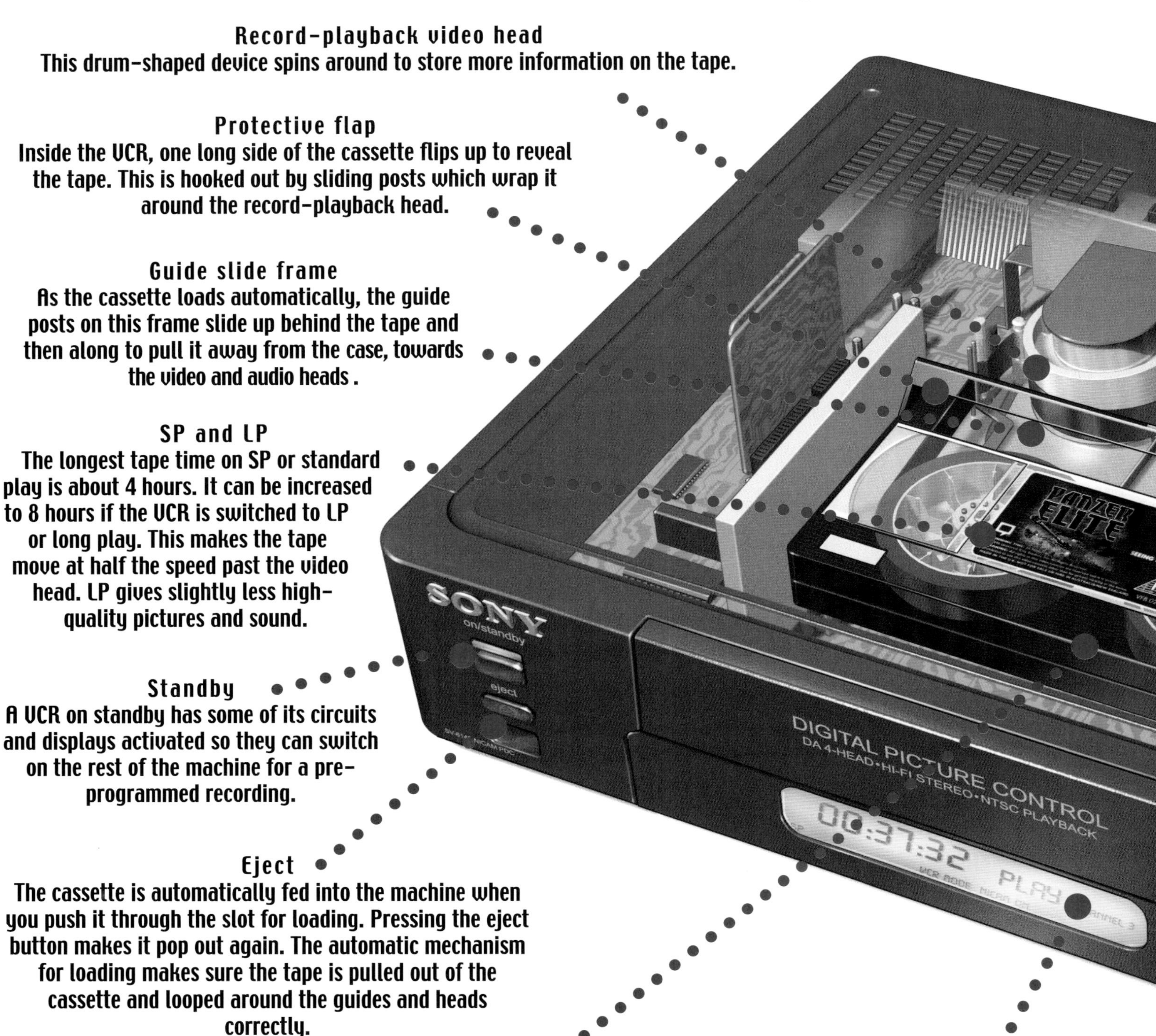

Record-playback video head
This drum-shaped device spins around to store more information on the tape.

Protective flap
Inside the VCR, one long side of the cassette flips up to reveal the tape. This is hooked out by sliding posts which wrap it around the record-playback head.

Guide slide frame
As the cassette loads automatically, the guide posts on this frame slide up behind the tape and then along to pull it away from the case, towards the video and audio heads.

SP and LP
The longest tape time on SP or standard play is about 4 hours. It can be increased to 8 hours if the VCR is switched to LP or long play. This makes the tape move at half the speed past the video head. LP gives slightly less high-quality pictures and sound.

Standby
A VCR on standby has some of its circuits and displays activated so they can switch on the rest of the machine for a pre-programmed recording.

Eject
The cassette is automatically fed into the machine when you push it through the slot for loading. Pressing the eject button makes it pop out again. The automatic mechanism for loading makes sure the tape is pulled out of the cassette and looped around the guides and heads correctly.

Video cassette
Video tape is almost 13 millimetres (half an inch) wide. It has various layers like an audio tape. The thinner the base layer of the tape, the more tape can be fitted into the cassette, usually up to about 300 metres (984 feet).

Display
Numbers and symbols on the display show information such as the time, the TV channel or programme selected, the amount of tape time that has passed or is left, and whether the tape is playing, recording or fast-winding.

SPINNING HELICAL HEAD

A TV does not show moving pictures. It displays 25–30 still pictures each second. These come and go so quickly that they blur together to give an illusion of continuous movement. Also, each picture on the screen is not made of areas of continuous colour. It is a mosaic of hundreds of thousands of tiny units, which again are blurred by the eye to look like continuous colours.

To record and play back so much information the VCR has a helical spinning video head. This turns in the opposite direction to the tape that slides past it. So the speed of the tape moving past the head is effectively increased, and this allows more information to be packed in. The information is recorded as a series of helical strips, like a diagonal corkscrew pattern, which again allows more information to be stored.

Connectors
At the rear of the VCR are sockets and connectors for electrical signals coming in from the terrestrial aerial or satellite system, out to the television or monitor screens and out to a surround sound or full hi-fi system.

Record-playback audio head
The audio head deals with the electrical signals for sounds, which are separate from those for the pictures.

Drive capstan
As in an audio cassette player, the capstan has the tape pressed against it by the pinch wheel and rotates to make the tape move along past it at a constant speed.

Power supply transformer
The transformer reduces the high voltage from mains electricity to much lower voltages for the electronic circuits in the VCR.

Tuner
Most VCRs now have automatic set-up. When this is activated the tuning circuits scan all the incoming TV signal channels, identify those which are strong enough to give a good-quality picture and sound, and lock these into the memory.

Cassette tray
The cassette feeds through the loading slot on to this tray, which carries it down and back into position for the tape to be exposed.

OTR
One-touch recording or OTR is a simple one-press button that starts the VCR recording whichever channel is selected at the time.

Main control button
The four major tape controls – play, stop, fast forward wind and fast rewind – are activated by pressing the sides of one large button. These and more controls are also on the remote control handset.

CAMERA

Shutter release
Pressing this button makes the swinging mirror tilt up out of the way and then opens the shutter for a brief time so light rays can shine past and reach the photographic film.

Shutter speed control
The dial or button manually adjusts the amount of time that the shutter is open so light can shine on to the film. In normal use this could be as little as 1/1000th of a second or as long as 1/60th of a second. Many modern cameras have automatic shutter speed control too.

Aperture control
This ring makes the hole in the iris bigger or smaller, to let more or less light through to the film. Many modern cameras have automatic aperture control, too.

Case
The case must be strong and light-proof because any stray light rays that enter will affect or fog the photographic film.

Manual focus
The main lenses can be moved manually by turning this ring, to focus the scene instead of using autofocus.

Main lenses
There are several objective lenses that gather and bend or focus the light so that blurring, haloes, coloured fringes and other distortions are as small as possible.

Pentaprism
This five-sided glass block turns the scene or image, reflected from the mirror below, the right way round and right way up. It then shines it through the viewfinder. So what you see is what will be in the photograph.

Iris
A ring of spiral flaps twists to make the hole at its centre, the aperture, larger or smaller. This lets more or less light through to the film. Because of the way lenses work, it does not make the scene larger or smaller. But a smaller aperture does make the whole scene more clearly in focus.

Autofocus drive
In some cameras an electric motor adjusts the main lenses so that the scene is sharp and clear (in focus).

Pictures of the Past

Cameras from years ago were often heavy, bulky and awkward to handle. They were very sensitive to changes in light levels and also to any shaking that could make the photo look blurred.

TYPES OF CAMERAS

• Movie (cine) camera: The roll of photographic film goes past the shutter quickly and lots of still or stationary photos are taken very rapidly one after the other, many every second. When played back the images blur together and give the impression of movement, as on a TV screen.

• Camcorder: A camera that records movie-style 'moving pictures' but on video-type magnetic tape.

Hotshoe
A flash unit slides into this. The button in the middle of the shoe touches a contact on the base of the flash unit so that when the shutter release button is pressed, the light flashes at precisely the correct time to make the scene brighter.

Viewfinder
When you look through here you see exactly the view that will appear in the photograph, through the main lens. So you can check that the scene is clear and sharp (in focus), and that it is precisely the area you want to see (it is framed properly). In some cameras the viewfinder has a separate lens and is not an accurate representation of what will be in the eventual photograph.

Viewfinder meters
In the viewfinder there are display readouts, meters or scales around the edges of the scene. You can check the exposure or light level, the shutter speed (how long the film will be exposed), the battery strength and so on.

Rewind button
When all of the film is used up and the roll is on the take-up spool, this button makes a motor turn the supply spool so that the film winds backwards on to it. The spool can then be removed and a new film fitted.

Swinging mirror
Normally the mirror reflects light rays that come in through the main lenses, up through the pentaprism and into your eyes. When you take a photo the mirror swings up out of the way so that the light rays can shine briefly on to the photographic film.

Motor drive wind-on
When a photo is taken, an electric motor turns sprockets which pull or wind on the film on to the take-up spool by the right amount. Then a fresh blank area is ready for the next photo.

Film
The photographic film has light-sensitive chemicals on a flexible plastic base. It is in a long ribbon or roll and gear teeth (sprocket teeth) fit into holes along each edge to wind the film along for the next photograph.

SMILE FOR THE CAMERA!

More types of cameras include:

• SLR camera: SLR means single lens reflex (as shown in the diagram here).

• Compact: A simpler type of camera where the viewfinder is separate from the main lenses. It usually has fewer controls or automatic gadgets than an SLR camera.

• Disposable: An even simpler compact camera with built-in battery and film. When the roll of film is finished you hand in the whole camera for the film to be processed.

• Instant camera: A sheet of photographic film slides out of the camera after you take the photo. Chemicals built into it make the photo appear or develop in seconds.

CAMCORDER

Zoom lens system
There are many lenses in groups along this lens system. Zooming means they move in and out to change the field or area of view. Zooming in is like looking through a telescope – it shows a small area greatly enlarged. Zooming out shows a broader view at less magnification, so the scene looks further away.

Video tape
The electronic signals from the CCD circuits (representing the picture) and microphones (the sound) are recorded on a video tape in the same way as for a VCR. In some designs the cassette is removed. In others the camcorder is plugged into a VCR later to transfer the recording.

Objective
The large lenses at the front are called the objective because they point at the object – the item or scene that is being recorded. They gather light rays from the scene and begin to bend or focus them as they pass through the lens system inside the camera.

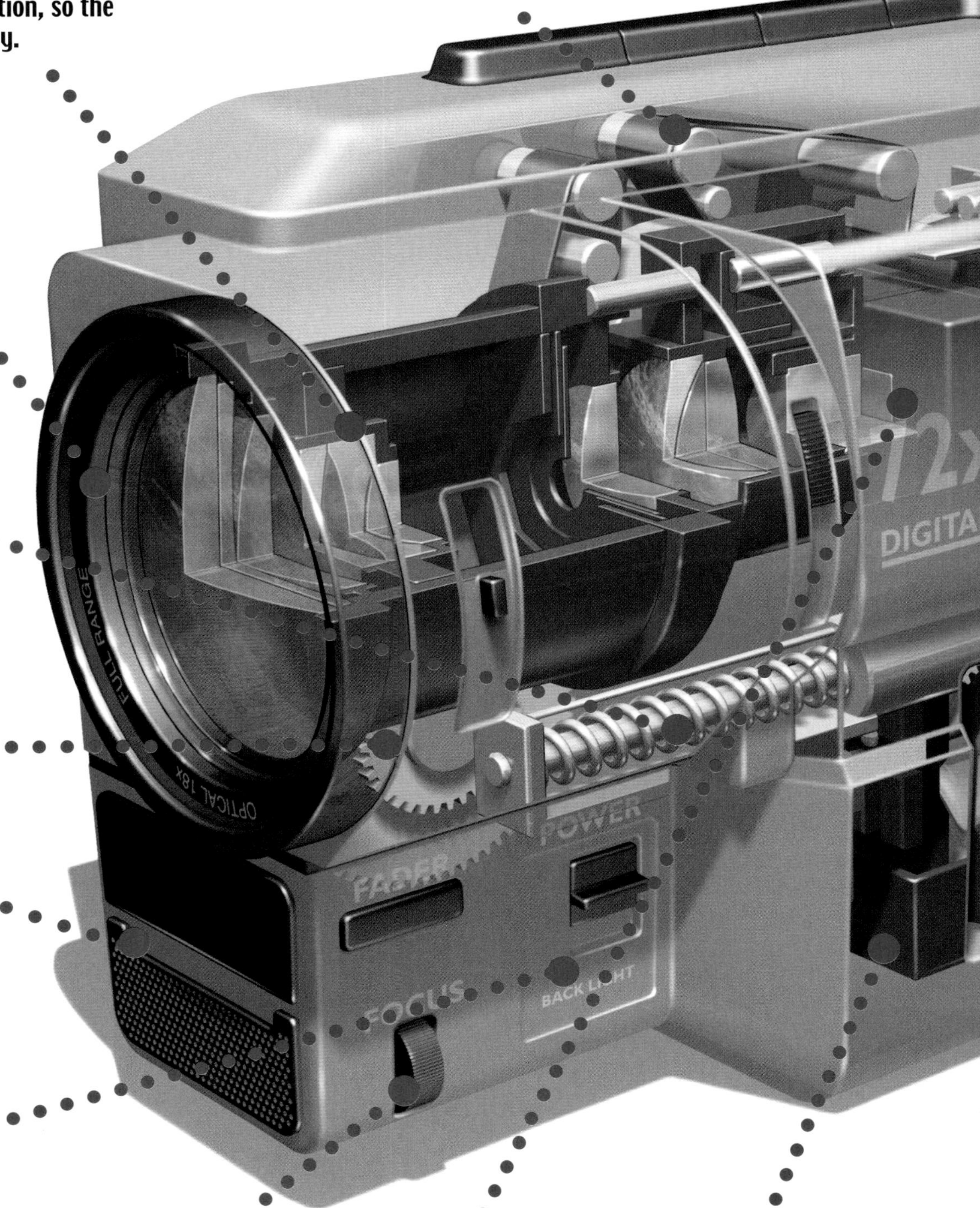

Zoom return
A spring on a sliding rod makes sure that the lens system slides smoothly for zooming in and out.

Zoom gearing
This moves the main lens system forwards and backwards to zoom the image in and out.

Microphone
Two small microphones angled to each side behind the protective grill detect stereo sound, which is recorded on the tape.

Screen backlight
This switches on the backlight for the screen so that it can be viewed in dull conditions. It can be switched off in bright conditions to save power, when the LCD screen works by reflected light.

Focus
The focus knob moves the lenses in relation to each other to make the picture clear and sharp.

CCD
The charge coupled device (CCD) is like a miniature screen that senses light rays and turns their positions and brightnesses into patterns of digital electronic signals.

Powerpack
A pack of rechargeable batteries provides power for the motors of the tape recorder and lens movements and for the electronic circuits and display screen.

Eyepiece
The user looks through this to see the viewfinder, which shows the pictures that the camcorder is taking.

Viewfinder
Unlike the photographic camera, light rays don't come all the way through the camcorder, so the user cannot see the scene. Instead, a miniature TV screen in the viewfinder shows the user what is being filmed.

CAMERA-RECORDER

A camcorder is a combination of a video camera and video recorder. The video camera is designed to take many still pictures or images (usually 25) each second. When they are played back they give the impression of continuous movement as on a TV screen. There is no photographic film in a camcorder as there is in a movie camera. The patterns of light rays that form the images are converted into corresponding patterns of electronic signals by components called CCDs, charge coupled devices. The signals are then recorded as tiny patches of magnetism on to a video tape.

Display screen
Pictures recorded on the tape can be played back for several viewers on the LCD screen. They can either be saved, or stored for later use to save tape time, or wiped and recorded over if they are not wanted.

THE SHRINKING CAMCORDER

Early camcorders were so heavy that they had to be held steady with two hands. They were complicated to use and worked only in bright light. Today's versions fit into the palm of the hand. They have simple controls with auto-focus and auto-exposure to adjust the camcorder to suit the changing brightness of the light. They work even in light levels that are almost too dim for the human eye.

HI-FI SYSTEM

Crossover circuit
The electronic crossover separates the electrical signals from the amplifier into high and low frequencies and feeds each set to the correct loudspeakers in the speaker enclosure or 'box'.

Tuner and preamp unit
The tuner tunes into and receives radio broadcasts. It has a built-in rod aerial to receive AM programmes and a socket or length of wire at the rear as an aerial for FM stations. The preamplifier (preamp) alters the electric signals from any input or source such as the tuner, tape or CD player, for example making them louder and with more bass or low notes, before feeding them into the main amplifier.

Digital display
This shows information as numbers, such as the track number and time from the CD-MD player, or the radio station being received by the tuner.

Program presets
Different radio stations or programmes can be locked into the memory so that you don't have to re-tune the radio tuner each time when changing stations.

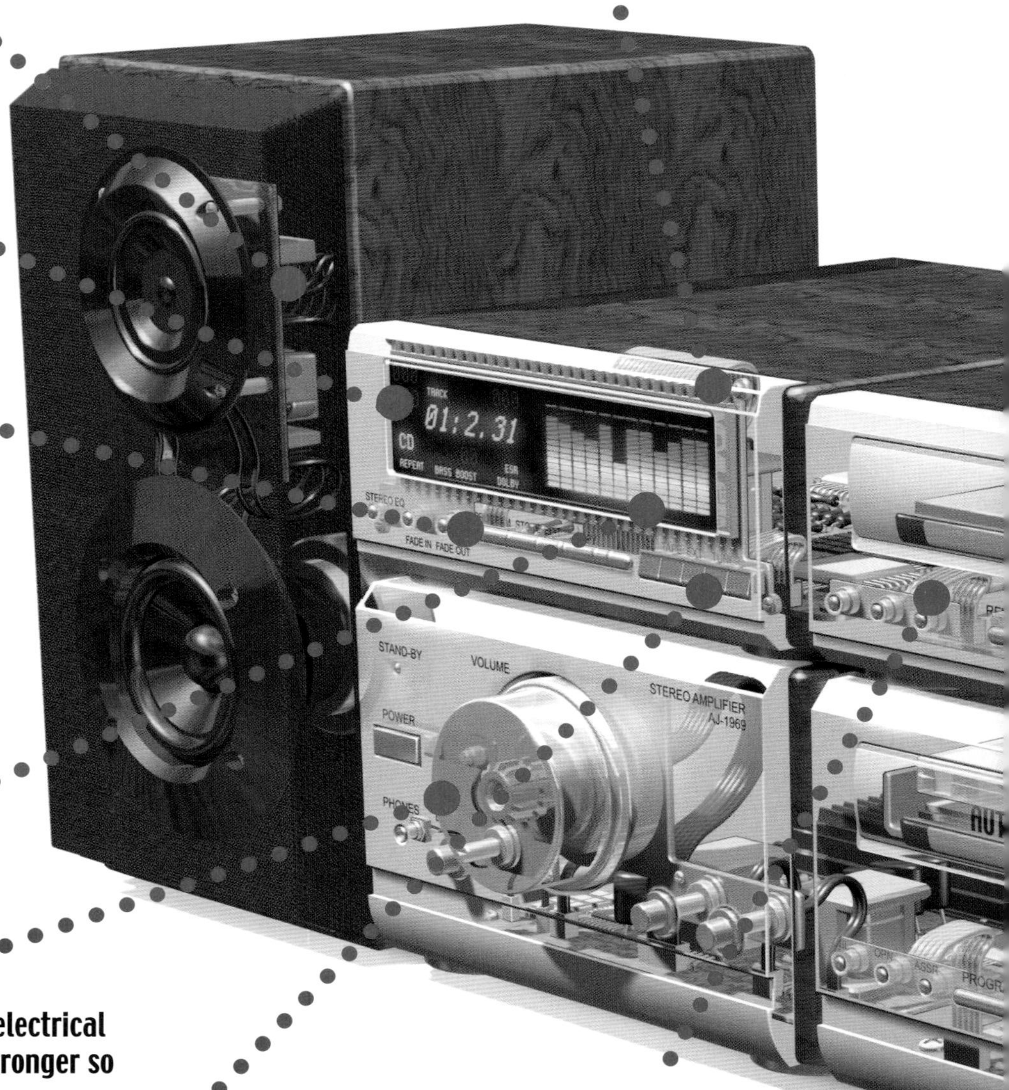

Graphic display
A graphic display shows information in visual form but without numbers. The coloured bars represent signals being sent from the preamplifier to the amplifier or from the amplifier to the speakers. Low or deep notes (LF, low frequency) are on the left and they get higher or shriller (HF, high frequency) towards the right.

Amplifier unit
The amplifier has the simple job of making the electrical signals it receives from the preamplifier much stronger so that they can power the loudspeakers.

Input (source) selector
These buttons select which unit feeds or inputs its signals to the preamplifier – that is, the source of the sound. It may be the system's CD-MD, the tape or tuner, or an external source (EXT) such as a microphone, vinyl record player or VCR attached by wires to the back of the system.

Skip and search
The user can jump or skip straight to the next or previous track on the CD, or move quickly forwards or backwards through the current track while still listening to the 'high-speed' version, to search for a particular part.

WHAT IS 'HI-FI'?

It means high fidelity, which is a certain standard of high quality, clear, undistorted sound. But the term 'hi-fi' has entered everyday language and is often used to mean almost any equipment on which music is played.

FM AND AM

FM or frequency modulation, and AM or amplitude modulation, are ways in which information is carried by radio signals in the form of waves. In FM the number or frequency of waves per second is altered or varied (modulated) slightly in an ongoing pattern. In AM the height or amplitude of the waves is modulated. The pattern of modulation is a code to carry the information.

AM sound may be muffled and distorted and is not in stereo, but it is usually easy to pick up. FM produces much clearer sounds in stereo but may not be easy to receive in certain areas.

CD-MD unit
The compact disc player accepts audio compact discs, CDs, which can contain up to about 75 minutes of full-quality music or other sounds. Some CD players also accept mini discs, MDs. These work in the same way but are smaller than CDs. They are used more for recording since they are digital and so of higher quality than audio cassettes.

Speaker cabinet
The cabinet is usually made of heavy, dense material to hold the loudspeakers firmly and produce the clearest sounds, especially of low notes. Its size and air space are carefully calculated so that it does not buzz or vibrate (resonate) and make certain frequencies unnaturally loud.

HF speaker (tweeter)
The small loudspeaker is designed to produce high-pitched or HF (high frequency) notes, such as the upper range of the human voice, trumpets, acoustic guitars, flutes, cymbals and birdsong.

LF speaker (woofer)
The large loudspeaker is for low-pitched or LF (low frequency) notes, such as the deeper range of the human voice, bass guitars, drums, tubas and trumpeting elephants.

Tape controls
These play, pause, stop, fast-forward wind and fast rewind the audio cassette. When recording, the tape can be set to begin as soon as the input or source starts feeding through its signals.

Tape deck
The audio cassette is played in this unit. When the tape finishes at one end it automatically moves in reverse to play the other 'side'.

GAMES CONSOLE

Memory card
This small plug-in memory device receives and stores information fed into it, or written to it, from the console. It might be a game or the current scores of each player and where they got to in the game during one play session. The card can then be unplugged. At a later date it is plugged in again and the information read back into the console, so the players can continue where they left off last time.

Select and start
Once the cursor or highlighted part of the screen is on the desired option, the selector chooses it and gets it ready to start. The start button begins the game.

Cursor movers
These buttons move a cursor, highlighted area or special symbol around the screen – up, down, left or right.

Special function buttons
These have special jobs or tasks according to the individual game. They may fire a weapon or allow you to jump from one place to another.

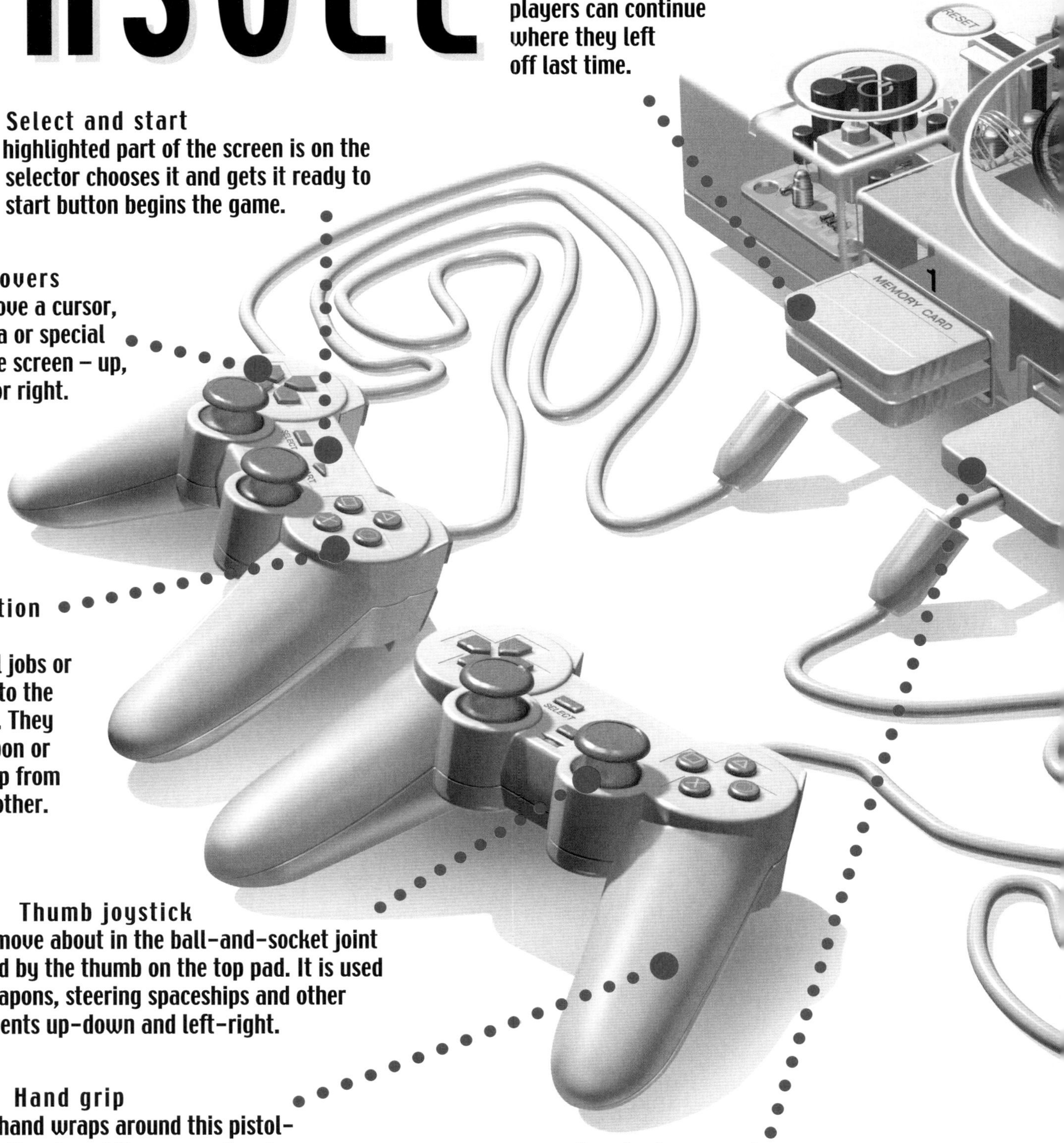

Thumb joystick
The joystick can move about in the ball-and-socket joint at its base, worked by the thumb on the top pad. It is used for aiming weapons, steering spaceships and other movements up-down and left-right.

Hand grip
The palm of the hand wraps around this pistol-type grip so the thumb and fingers are free to operate the joystick and buttons.

Handset connector
The handset plugs into the console. One or two players can play each other or work as a team against the machine.

GAMES FOR REAL
Computer games are fun and they can also have a useful and more serious side. Sims (simulations) are games that mimic or copy real-life activities such as playing golf, running a business, organizing a hospital, managing a sports team or surviving on a desert island. Playing the game can be good practice and help you to prepare for the real thing later – should you ever be stuck on a desert island!

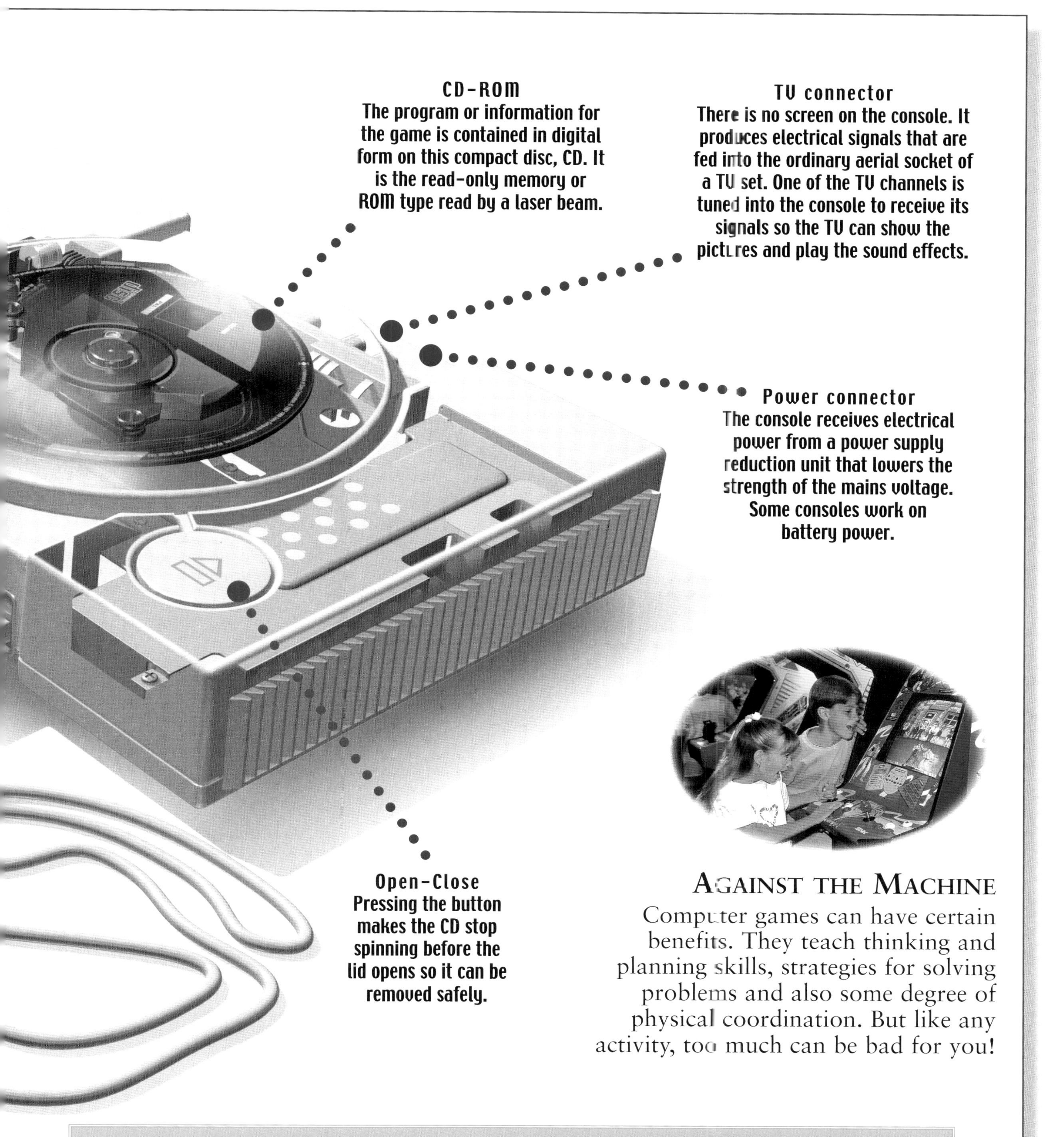

Against the Machine

Computer games can have certain benefits. They teach thinking and planning skills, strategies for solving problems and also some degree of physical coordination. But like any activity, too much can be bad for you!

FASTER AND BETTER

Games consoles from just a few years ago already look very old-fashioned. They work slowly and have simple graphics. In a few years' time, we will look back at today's most modern versions and think exactly the same. This shows the speed of progress in electronic and computerized gadgets, which has been happening since the 1960s.

A general guideline is that microchips and electronic circuits double in speed and/or memory every 18 months, and become cheaper to manufacture, too. This allows the colours and shapes on the games console screen to be clearer, sharper, more colourful and more realistic. People, animals, aliens and vehicles can move around the screen in more complicated ways. It also allows the games themselves to have more options, levels and possibilities.

VR HEADSET

Headset
The computer sends electrical signals to the headset screens which convert these into light rays. The user sees the patterns of rays with his or her eyes and understands them as a scene in his or her brain.

Topstrap
A wide strap passes over the top of the head to join the backstrap at the rear, so that the headset is comfortable.

Screens
The screens show the images or pictures for the eyes. They show slightly different images for each eye. In real life the two eyes see slightly different views since they look at the scene from slightly different places and directions.

Audio controls
The audio knobs control the volume of the stereo sound, its balance (whether it is too loud in the left or right ear), and its tone of high and low notes.

3-D vision
In the vision centres at the back of the user's brain, the two slightly different views from the two eyes are merged to give a single view in the 'mind's eye'. This has width, height and also depth or the illusion of distance. It is three-dimensional or 3-D stereoscopic vision.

Video controls
These knobs control the screen colour, brightness and contrast, as on a normal TV set.

Speaker
A speaker plays sounds directly into the ear on that side. Some headsets have earpieces or built-in headphones, which help to cut out unwanted sounds from around the user.

Strap adjuster
The straps are adjusted to suit the head size and shape of the individual user.

PCB
The main electronic components are fitted into a PCB, printed circuit board. This is made with metal strips already built or 'printed' into it. The components are then fitted on to the board so that the metal strips act as wires to connect them.

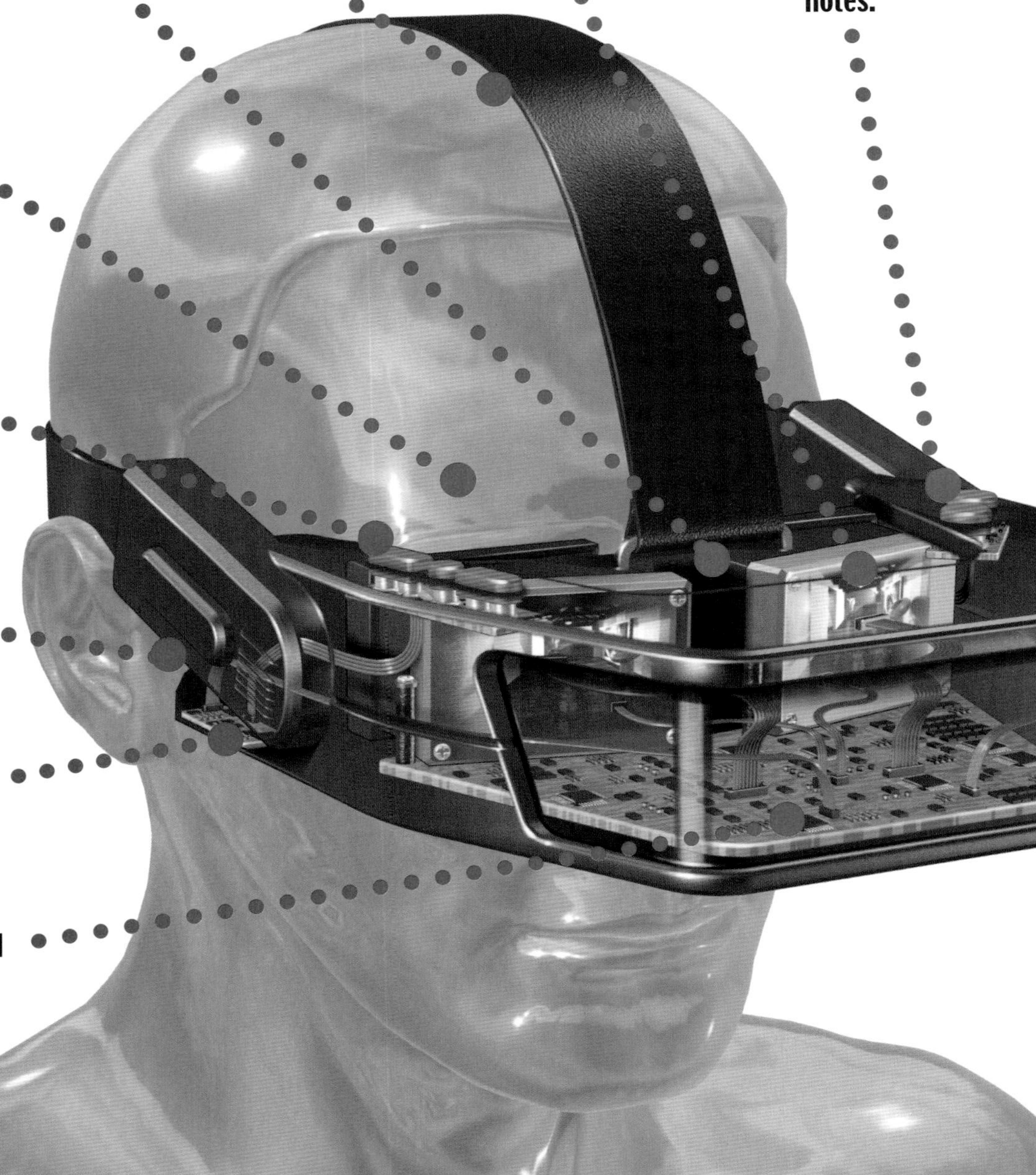

SERIOUS VR

VR systems vary from simple slip-on headsets to full helmets and body suits that look like deep-sea diving suits. These not only provide sight and sound but also physical pressure for the skin's sense of touch and perhaps scents for the nose, too. They also have feedback. They detect the user's movements, so that the computer can alter what he or she sees, hears and feels. The user seems to be moving about in a complete virtual world.

VR can be great fun for flying jet planes, shooting aliens and playing other games. But it also has many serious uses. It helps to train people such as pilots, surgeons, firefighters and rescue workers, where a mistake in the virtual world harms no one.

TAKING OFF TO NOWHERE

A form of VR has been used for many years in flight simulators where pilots train. The simulator is a whole room and the computer controls large motors or pistons that make it tilt and rock like a real aircraft.

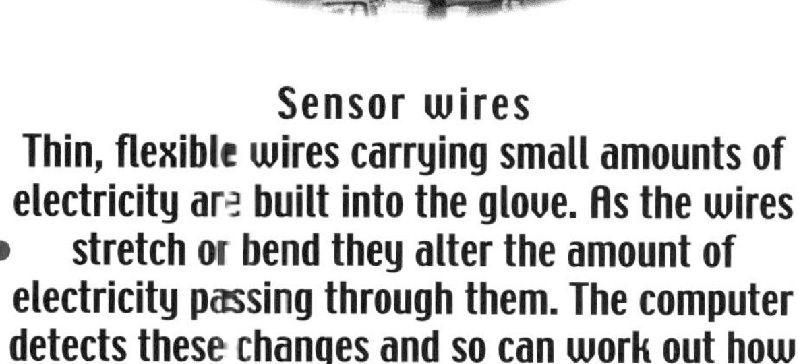

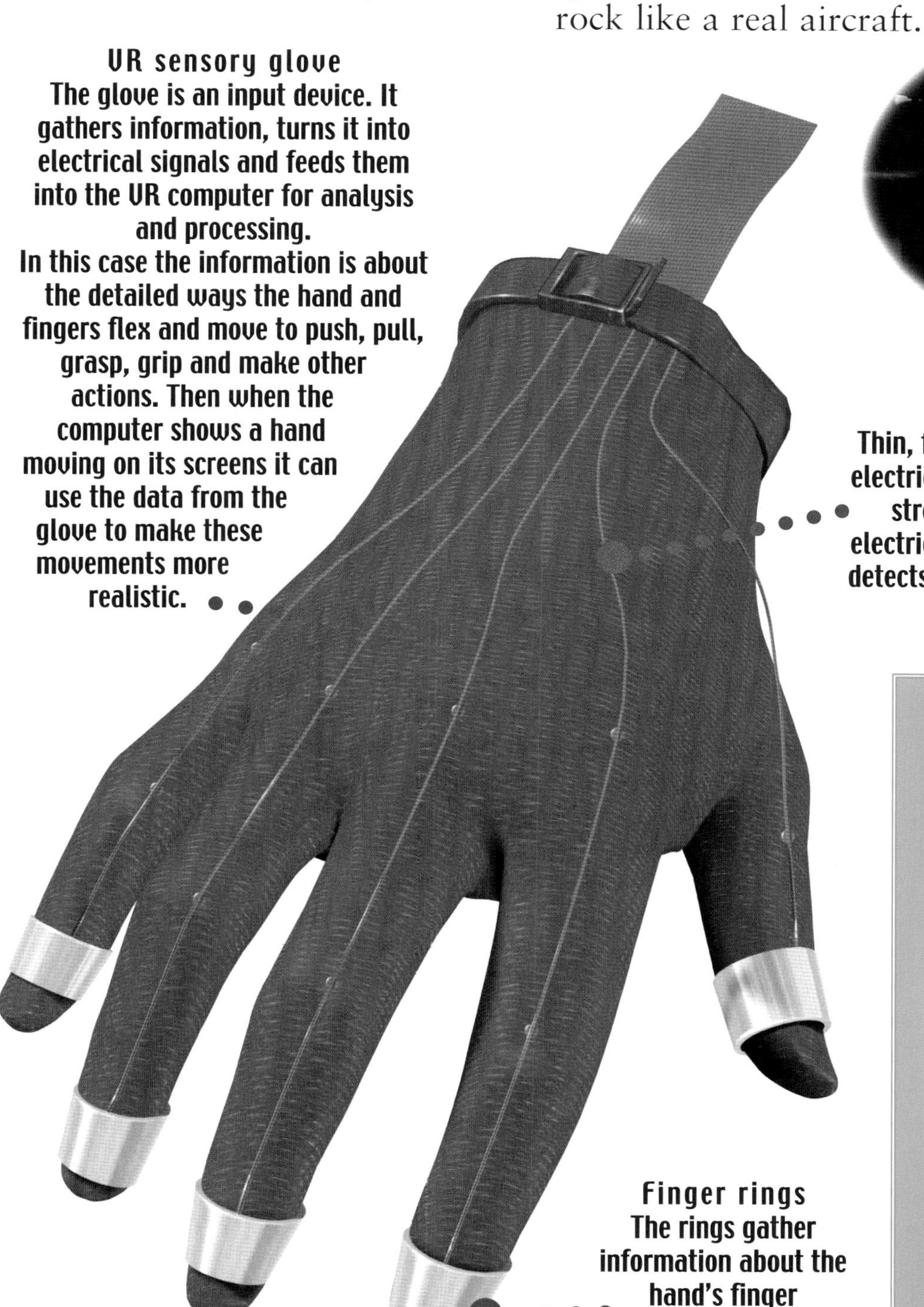

VR sensory glove
The glove is an input device. It gathers information, turns it into electrical signals and feeds them into the VR computer for analysis and processing.
In this case the information is about the detailed ways the hand and fingers flex and move to push, pull, grasp, grip and make other actions. Then when the computer shows a hand moving on its screens it can use the data from the glove to make these movements more realistic.

Sensor wires
Thin, flexible wires carrying small amounts of electricity are built into the glove. As the wires stretch or bend they alter the amount of electricity passing through them. The computer detects these changes and so can work out how the fingers are moving.

Finger rings
The rings gather information about the hand's finger movements and gripping pressure.

WHAT IS VIRTUAL REALITY?

It's an object or scene that seems real to the senses of sight, hearing, touch and smell, but is not. It is virtual, or unreal. It exists only as electronic signals in a computer and as spots of light on a screen, sound waves from an earpiece and other ways of stimulating our senses. A central computer processes all the information and sends out the signals to various pieces of equipment. These give us the illusion of seeing, hearing, touching and even smelling, and so we get a sense of reality.

CD PLAYER

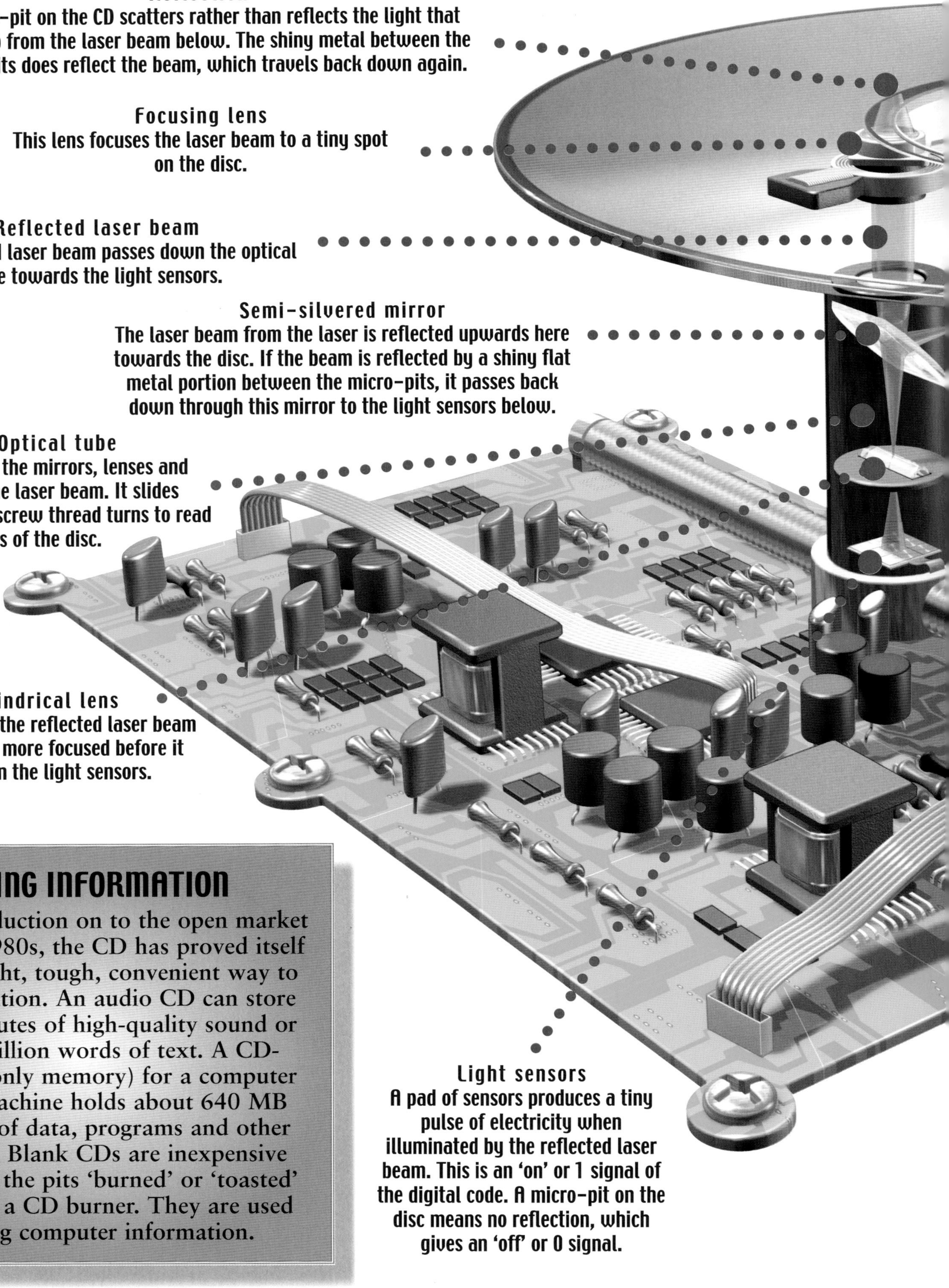

Reflection
A micro-pit on the CD scatters rather than reflects the light that shines up from the laser beam below. The shiny metal between the micro-pits does reflect the beam, which travels back down again.

Focusing lens
This lens focuses the laser beam to a tiny spot on the disc.

Reflected laser beam
The reflected laser beam passes down the optical tube towards the light sensors.

Semi-silvered mirror
The laser beam from the laser is reflected upwards here towards the disc. If the beam is reflected by a shiny flat metal portion between the micro-pits, it passes back down through this mirror to the light sensors below.

Optical tube
This contains the mirrors, lenses and sensors for the laser beam. It slides along as the screw thread turns to read different parts of the disc.

Cylindrical lens
A lens makes the reflected laser beam narrower or more focused before it shines on the light sensors.

Light sensors
A pad of sensors produces a tiny pulse of electricity when illuminated by the reflected laser beam. This is an 'on' or 1 signal of the digital code. A micro-pit on the disc means no reflection, which gives an 'off' or 0 signal.

STORING INFORMATION

Since its introduction on to the open market in the early 1980s, the CD has proved itself as a small, light, tough, convenient way to store information. An audio CD can store up to 75 minutes of high-quality sound or over 100 million words of text. A CD-ROM (read-only memory) for a computer or similar machine holds about 640 MB (megabytes) of data, programs and other information. Blank CDs are inexpensive and can have the pits 'burned' or 'toasted' into them by a CD burner. They are used for storing computer information.

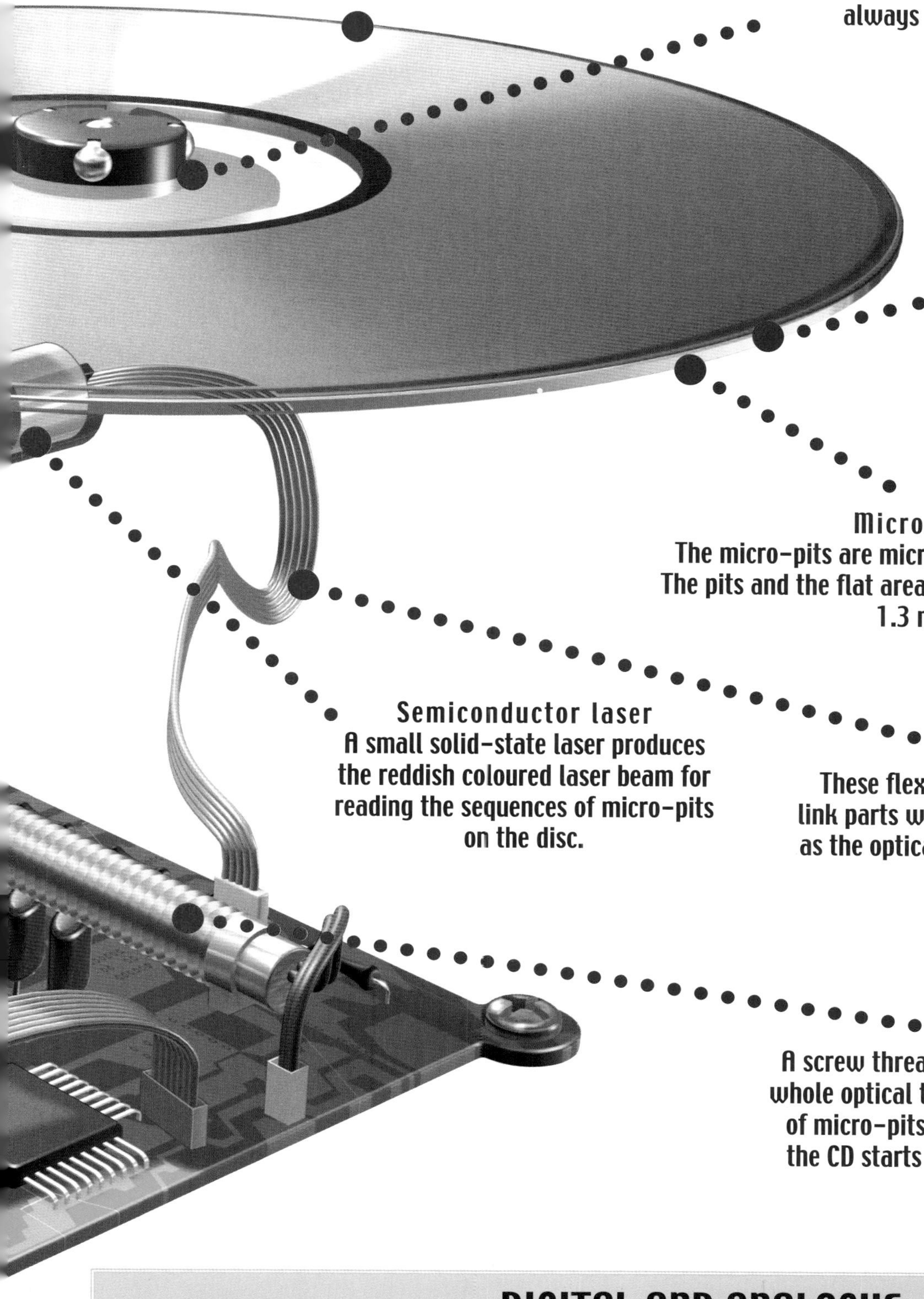

Compact disc
The disc is made mainly of plastic and is 12 centimetres (5 inches) across. The working part is its underside, which is coated with a thin layer of shiny aluminium-based metal.

CD drive motor
Under the CD is a variable speed motor that makes the disc spin around. A vinyl record spins at a constant speed, such as 33.3 turns or revolutions per minute (rpm) for a long player (LP). The CD turns at a varying speed according to whether the inside or outside part of the track is being read, so that the pits and flats always pass the laser beam at a constant rate.

CD track (underside)
As on a vinyl record, the CD track spirals out from the centre, round and round towards the edge. It is more than 5 kilometres (3 miles) long and contains more than 3 billion micro-pits. The sequence of micro-pits is a code for information.

Micro-pits (underside)
The micro-pits are microscopic holes or gaps in the CD track. The pits and the flat areas between them are read at the rate of 1.3 million per second.

Semiconductor laser
A small solid-state laser produces the reddish coloured laser beam for reading the sequences of micro-pits on the disc.

Ribbon connector
These flexible multi-wire connectors are used to link parts which move in relation to each other, such as the optical tube and the main circuit board in this CD player.

Optical drive screw
A screw thread turned by an electric motor moves the whole optical tube so that it follows the spiralling track of micro-pits as the disc spins. Unlike a vinyl record, the CD starts playing nearest the middle and finishes out at the edge.

DIGITAL AND ANALOGUE

The CD is digital. This means it stores information as a sequence or code of numbers or digits. In fact it has only two digits, 0 and 1. The 0 can be thought of as no reflection from the disc where there is a micro-pit. The 1 is a reflection where there isn't a micro-pit. Using two numbers is called binary code. Computers work using binary code, too, making CDs very useful for them.

Analogue systems do not use numbers or on-offs. They use continually varying quantities like a 'wave' of electrical voltage. Although the wave is meant to vary, much smaller natural variations occur within it and mean that it is not an exact way to carry information. As it is played or copied many times, the variations and errors can build up. Copying digital information means copying out lists of 0s and 1s, which is not prone to errors.

WIDESCREEN TV

Stereo sound
Two sets of loudspeakers play different sounds for the left and right channels. These reach our left and right ears and give the effect of sounds spread out in front of us across the breadth of the screen. This is known as stereophonic sound.

Wide sound
Extra loudspeakers positioned to the sides or rear help to spread out the sound. Sometimes a car or plane can be heard approaching from the side before it appears on the screen.

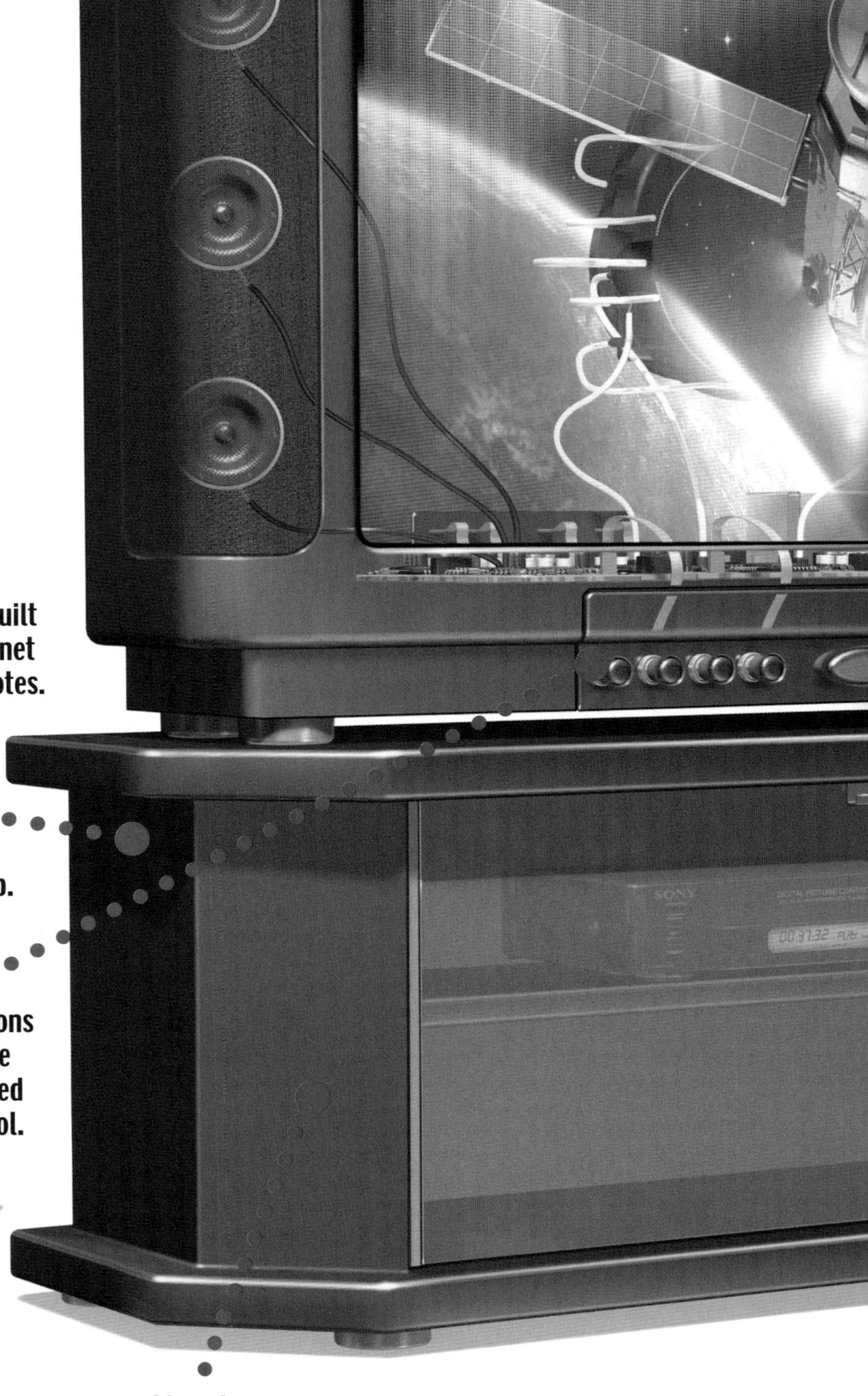

Subsound
A large loudspeaker built into the TV stand cabinet produces very deep notes. These are not so much heard as felt – for example, the rumble of an earthquake or the boom of a thunderclap.

Zoom control
The size and proportions of the picture on the screen can be changed with the zoom control.

Stand
The widescreen TV is very heavy. It has a strong, stable cabinet as a stand. This also stores a VCR and its videotape cassettes, a DVD player and its discs, and perhaps the week's television broadcast guide.

Pixels
A pixel or picture element is a tiny unit of the screen whose brightness and colour can be controlled. It consists of tiny dots that glow in different colours, red and green and blue. Pixels are built up like spots of colour in a mosaic to make the whole screen picture.

Picture quality
The quality of a TV picture depends on many features such as the quality of the original electrical signals and the number of lines on the screen. Standard TV screens have pictures made up of some 100,000 pixels arranged in 625 horizontal lines across the screen. The lines are scanned or made to glow from top to bottom.

TV SCREEN PROPORTIONS
The proportion or ratio of the screen is the length from side to side compared with the height from top to bottom. A typical TV is about 4:3 – that is, one-third again as wide as it is high. However, a full-sized movie screen in a cinema has the ratio 16:9, almost twice as wide as it is high. This was designed to fit comfortably into our field of vision or view, which is the area in front of us that our eyes can see and take in easily. It allows us to watch much broader, more spectacular scenes. Widescreen TV has similar proportions to a movie screen for the same spectacular effect.

HDTV
Picture quality improves with HD or high definition TV. The screen has more and closer-together horizontal lines, over 1,000, compared to the normal 625.

Wide screen
The screen is much wider than that of a conventional TV screen. Its proportions suit the natural field of view of our eyes better.

Words on-screen
Teletext may have over 1,000 pages of writing giving all kinds of information such as news headlines, sports results, weather forecasts and adverts for holidays, money loans and many other items.

VCR/DVD
If there are no suitable programmes on terrestrial, satellite or cable TV, the VCR (video cassette recorder-player) and DVD (digital versatile disk player) can show pre-recorded programmes.

TV SCREEN SIZES
The size of a TV or monitor screen is usually measured diagonally, from one top corner to the bottom opposite corner. However, the edges of the screen may be covered by the frame of the plastic case for the set, so the amount of screen that actually shows the picture is slightly less. A typical smallish 'portable' TV set screen is 35 centimetres (14 inches). A standard domestic TV may be 63 centimetres (25 inches). A widescreen TV may be 100 centimetres (40 inches) or more. The screen is the front of a glass part called a 'tube' (CRT, cathode ray tube or vacuum tube). It looks like a mushroom lying on its side with the 'stalk' projecting backwards. FST is a flatter, squarer tube. The screen surface is flat rather than slightly domed and has more angular rather than rounded corners.

PERSONAL COMPUTER (PC)

Computer tower
Most of the computer's circuits and drives are housed in a tower unit. This can be placed on a shelf or nearby table if there is not enough room on the desktop.

High capacity magnetic drive
Larger magnetic discs that hold more information are slotted in here.

Hard disc drive
The hard disc is really a stack of magnetic discs in a case. It is kept in the computer and holds all the computer's programs and data.

Magnetic disc drive
Removable discs can be placed in this drive. Information is fed from the computer, or written, to the disc and recorded as tiny patches of magnetism on the disc surface. Later the information may be read, or fed back into the computer. This means the discs are read-write rather than read-only.

Motherboard
The large printed circuit board contains most of the main microchips and components. They include the CPU or central processing unit, which is the computer's 'central brain', and the RAM or random access memory chips, which are its working memory.

Optical disc drive
Compact discs (CDs) are placed in this drive. They store information as patterns of microscopic pits on their surface and are read optically by laser light. Many computers have read-only optical drives. This means the information stored on them like a memory can only be taken from the disc into the computer. New information cannot be taken from the computer and stored on the disc. So the drive and discs are called CD-ROM, compact disc read-only memory.

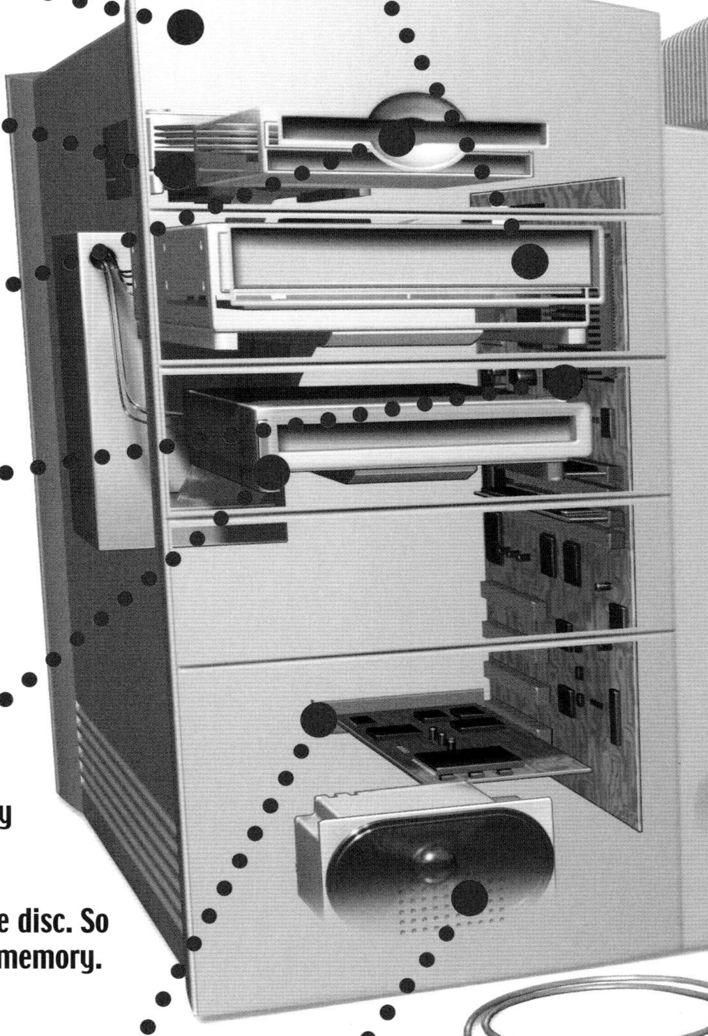

Rear panel
On panels at the back of the computer are sockets and connectors to link it by wires and cables to the monitor screen, keyboard, mouse and extra devices or peripherals.

Loudspeaker
The computer may be able to play music from its discs or programs. It also makes various beeps, pings and other sounds. These show that it is working properly, has completed a task or is unable to carry out some process.

Mouse
Moving the mouse moves a pointer or cursor on the screen on to various choices, options, lists and menus. Clicking a button on the mouse selects that choice or option. In image-based programs the mouse can be used like a pen to draw and alter pictures.

Mouse mat
This gives a flat but grippy surface for the mouse to roll on. A rubber ball inside the mouse must roll for the mouse to work.

ADD-ONS

A basic computer usually has a main unit with the circuits and drives, a keyboard, a mouse and a monitor screen. The main unit and screen may be in the same case. But there are dozens of add-ons, plug-ins or peripherals that can be connected to the computer. A common one is the printer to produce 'hard copy' – writing or pictures on paper rather than on the screen. Others that input or send signals to the computer include an image scanner, microphone, digital camera, joystick and music keyboard. Then there are outputs, which receive signals from the computer. These include a hi-fi system, a large and accurate printer called a plotter, image projector and a moving robot arm.

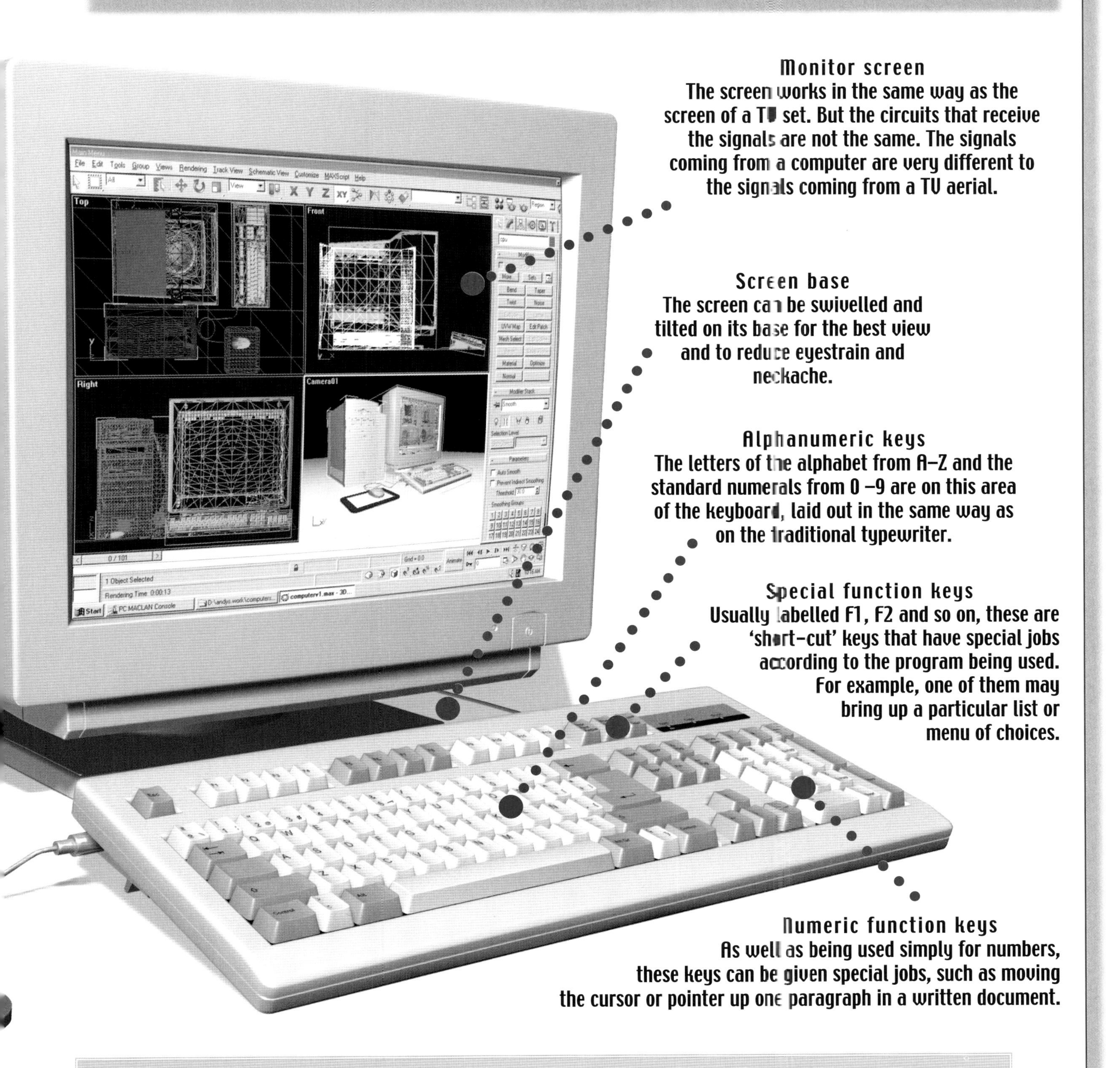

COMPUTER TERMINALS

The computer shown here is a complete working unit and can be used on its own. A computer terminal may look similar. But it is usually just a screen, keyboard and mouse. These are connected by longer wires or a network to a main computer. Many other terminals are connected too. Lots of people can use the same computer at the same time, sharing the information and programs.

IMAGE SCANNER

Scan head drive
This toothed cog or gear wheel pulls on the belt and makes the scan head move along. It must work to very exact measurements since the scan head may slide along by only a tiny amount between each scanned line.

Hinged lid
The lid protects the glass platen beneath to keep it clean, and presses down the paper or card carrying images to be scanned on to the glass so that they are sharp and in focus.

Connectors
The rear of the machine has various sockets and connectors for the power supply and the cable to the computer.

Scan drive motor
The motor turns by minute, precise amounts. It moves the scan head along fractionally, stops while the line is scanned, and then does the same again, moving many thousands of times to scan one page.

Slide groove
The end of the scan head slides along in this groove. It must be extremely smooth and free from dirt or dust, or the scan head will twist or jump.

Scan head
The scanning beam lights and sensors are contained in the scan head, which slides along the machine from back to front while scanning.

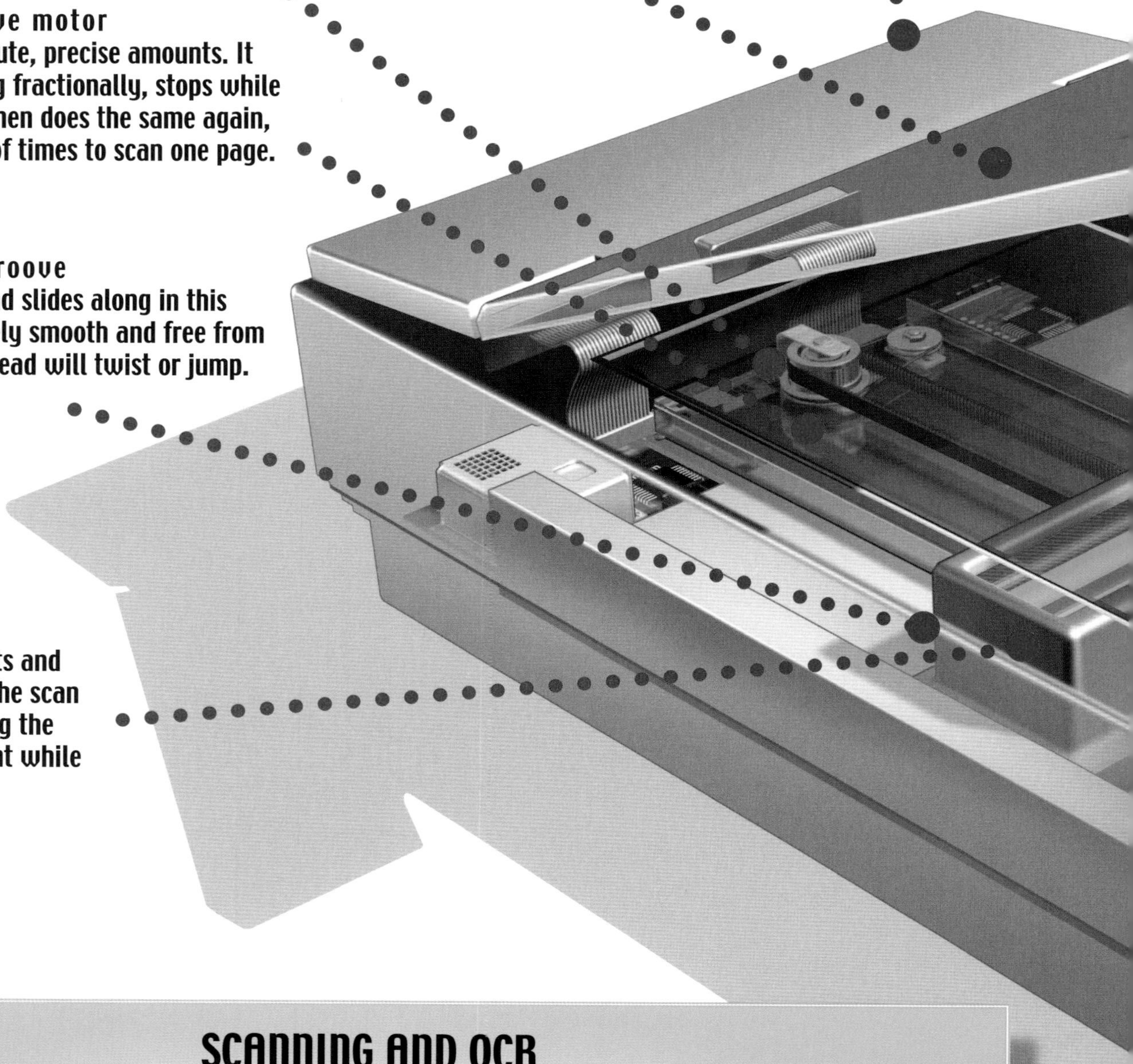

SCANNING AND OCR

Image scanners scan any images or pictures such as drawings, sketches, diagrams, paintings and photographs. They convert them into a series of digital electronic pulses that can be fed into a computer. This is called digitizing the image.

Scanners can scan writing, too, and feed it into the computer. But normally the computer would not understand the shape of, for example, the letter A as the actual letter A, the first letter of the alphabet. The A from a scanner is just a series of lines – a shape. It is not the same code as the letter A typed in from the keyboard.

However, some scanners and computers have OCR programs, optical character recognition. The program looks for certain patterns of lines, recognizes them as a letter such as A, and converts the digital code of the shape into the digital code for that letter. In this way the computer can almost 'read'.

HOW SCANNERS SCANS

A scanner records its first very straight, thin line across the top of the image. It measures the image's colour and brightness at points along this line. It then moves itself or the image slightly and records another straight line right next to the first. It repeats these actions to build up a point by point, line by line representation of the image.

The distance between the points and lines is called the resolution. The smaller the distance, the higher the resolution, and the clearer the picture. Low resolution gives a spotty, coarse, mosaic-like appearance.

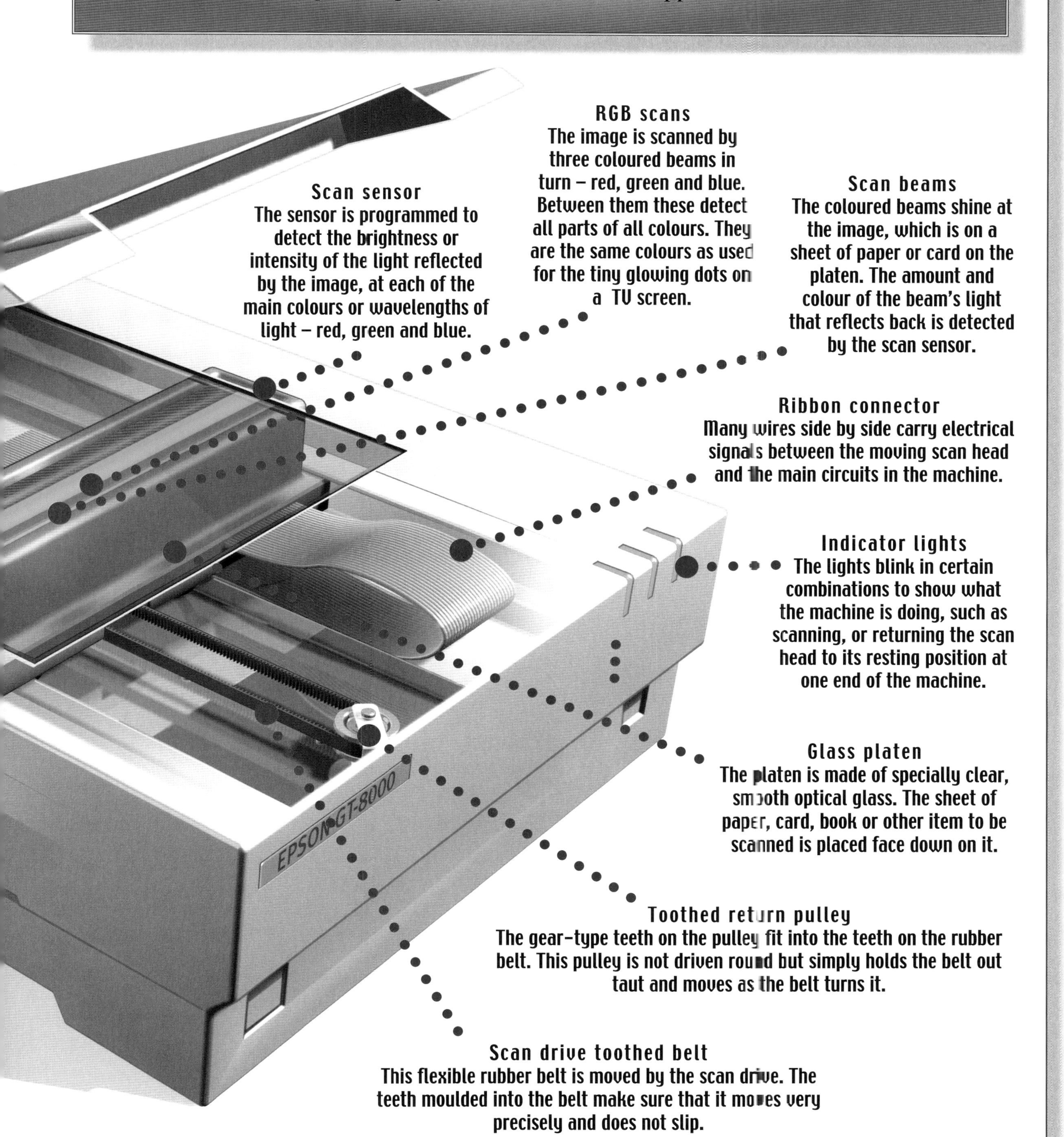

RGB scans
The image is scanned by three coloured beams in turn – red, green and blue. Between them these detect all parts of all colours. They are the same colours as used for the tiny glowing dots on a TV screen.

Scan sensor
The sensor is programmed to detect the brightness or intensity of the light reflected by the image, at each of the main colours or wavelengths of light – red, green and blue.

Scan beams
The coloured beams shine at the image, which is on a sheet of paper or card on the platen. The amount and colour of the beam's light that reflects back is detected by the scan sensor.

Ribbon connector
Many wires side by side carry electrical signals between the moving scan head and the main circuits in the machine.

Indicator lights
The lights blink in certain combinations to show what the machine is doing, such as scanning, or returning the scan head to its resting position at one end of the machine.

Glass platen
The platen is made of specially clear, smooth optical glass. The sheet of paper, card, book or other item to be scanned is placed face down on it.

Toothed return pulley
The gear-type teeth on the pulley fit into the teeth on the rubber belt. This pulley is not driven round but simply holds the belt out taut and moves as the belt turns it.

Scan drive toothed belt
This flexible rubber belt is moved by the scan drive. The teeth moulded into the belt make sure that it moves very precisely and does not slip.

FAX MACHINE

INSTANT PICTURES

Fax machines are especially useful for sending pictures, diagrams and sketches. Almost as the paper feeds through the sending machine, the receiving machine prints out the same thing at the other end of the phone line.

Digital display
Various numbers are shown on the display, such as the telephone number of the fax machine you are sending to or the telephone number of the fax machine sending you a document.

Program buttons
These buttons program instructions and information into the machine's memory, such as the number of times the phone rings before the fax machine or answerphone cuts in to answer it.

Number pad
Telephone numbers are dialled by pressing the numbers on this pad. The buttons are also used to put instructions into the machine.

Handset
You can use this handset to make a telephone call and speak to the person at the other end in the normal way. But you can't do this while a fax is being sent.

Paper roller
The paper is for faxes which the machine receives and feeds out at the top.

Feed slot
The sheet of paper with the writing, drawing or other marks on it, that you want to send as a fax, is fed into this slot.

WHY 'FAX'?

The name is a shortened version of 'facsimile' which means an exact copy or duplicate. A document fed into a fax machine doesn't get rolled up and squeezed down the telephone line! The machine scans the document for dark marks, converts them into a series of electrical signals and sends them along the phone line to another fax machine. That machine prints the marks on to a clean sheet of paper. As the document passes through the sending machine its copy emerges from the receiving machine with only a split second delay. The sender still has the original document and the receiver has the copy or fax.

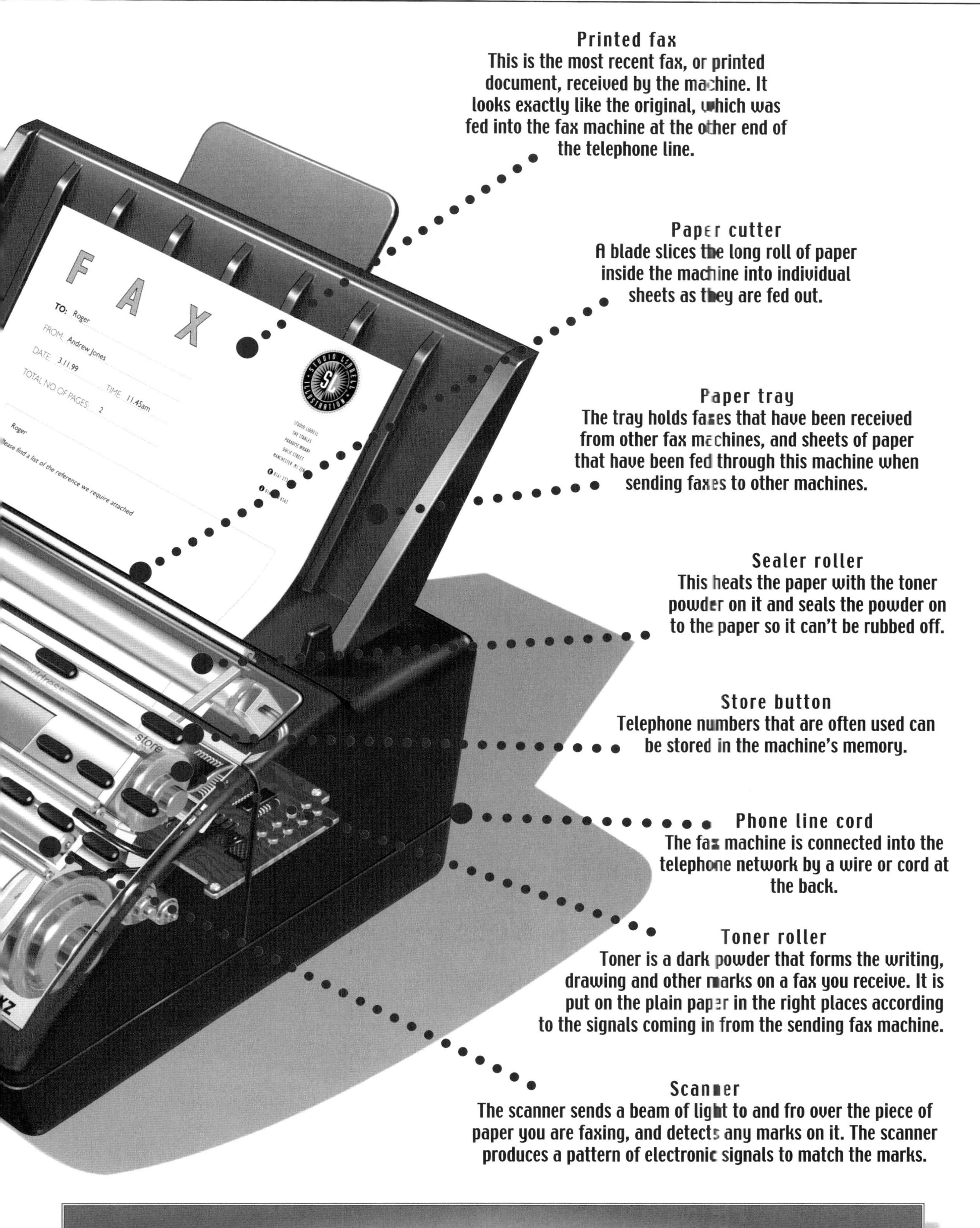

WHAT CAN I SEND BY FAX?

Any marks or dark patches on paper can be faxed. This includes handwriting, typewriting, printed pages from books and magazines, photocopies, drawings, illustrations, sketches, photographs, patterns and diagrams. Some faxes send and receive in black and white only. Others can do so in colour, but only if the machine at the other end also works in colour.

VIDEOPHONE

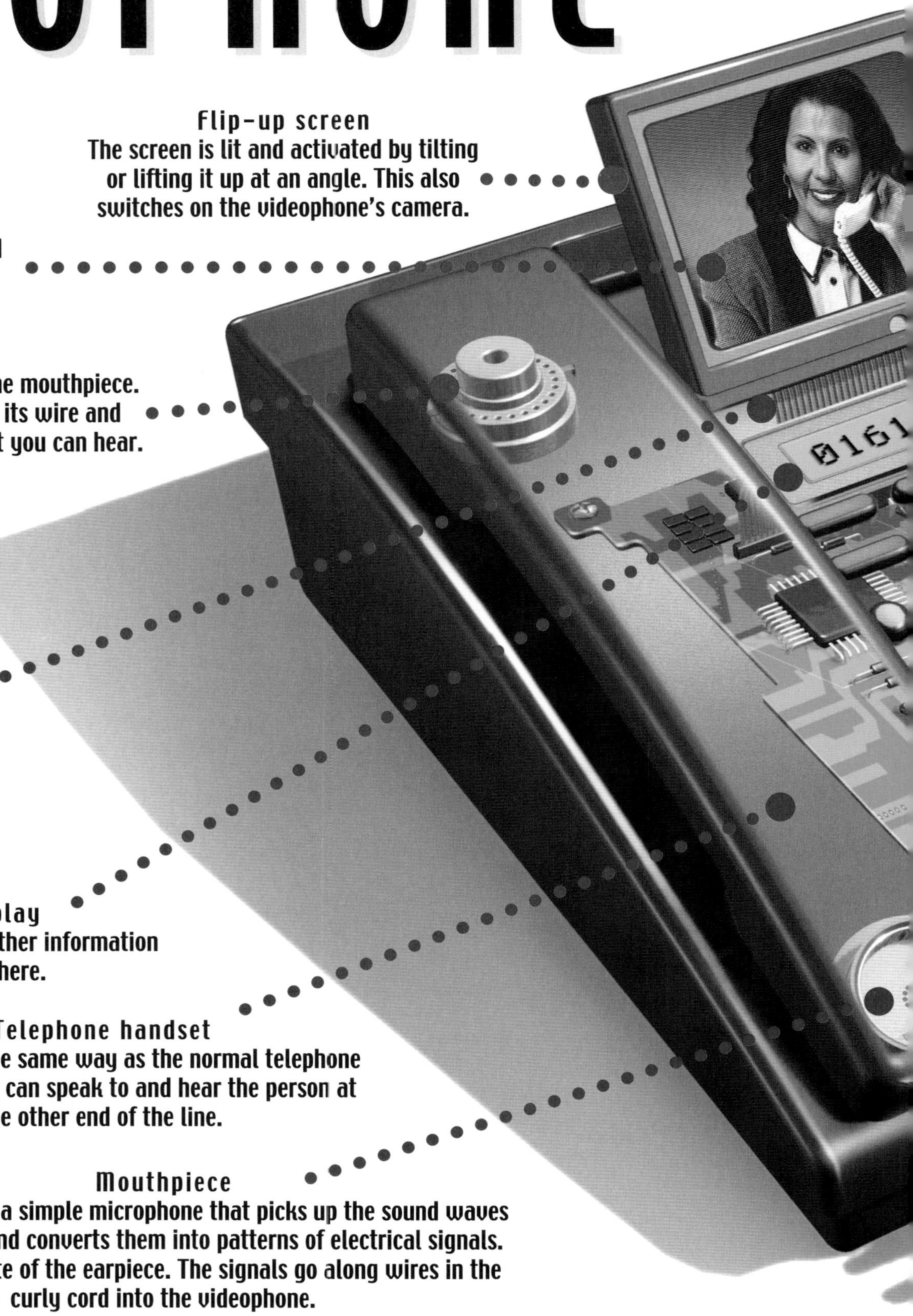

Flip-up screen
The screen is lit and activated by tilting or lifting it up at an angle. This also switches on the videophone's camera.

LCD
The small screen does not use a 'tube' like a normal television set. It has a much flatter, lighter liquid crystal display (LCD).

Earpiece
This works in the opposite way to the mouthpiece. It receives electrical signals along its wire and converts them into sound waves that you can hear.

Loudspeaker
The loudspeaker produces the sound of the other person's voice if the handset is not being used. It has to give out only a limited range of sound pitches or frequencies, those produced by the voice, compared to the music of a full orchestra. So it can be small and simple compared to a proper music system loudspeaker.

Digital display
Telephone numbers and other information are displayed here.

Telephone handset
This works in the same way as the normal telephone handset, so you can speak to and hear the person at the other end of the line.

Mouthpiece
The mouthpiece is a simple microphone that picks up the sound waves from your voice and converts them into patterns of electrical signals. This is the opposite of the earpiece. The signals go along wires in the curly cord into the videophone.

LCD TECHNOLOGY

A liquid crystal display (LCD) is much smaller, flatter and lighter than the 'tube' for a normal television screen. However, its picture isn't quite as sharp and clear. In an LCD tiny spots of coloured crystalline substances, like coloured jelly, let through or stop light by a certain amount according to how much electricity is passed through them. In the backlit display the light comes from the lowest or base layer of screen behind the crystals, passes through them and shines into the eyes. This is brighter than the non-backlit version, where light from the surroundings is reflected off the back of the screen. Most digital watches have non-backlit LCD displays. Backlit are used in laptop and palmtop computers, in miniature and wristwatch TVs, and in some giant screens at sports stadia, music concerts and similar big events.

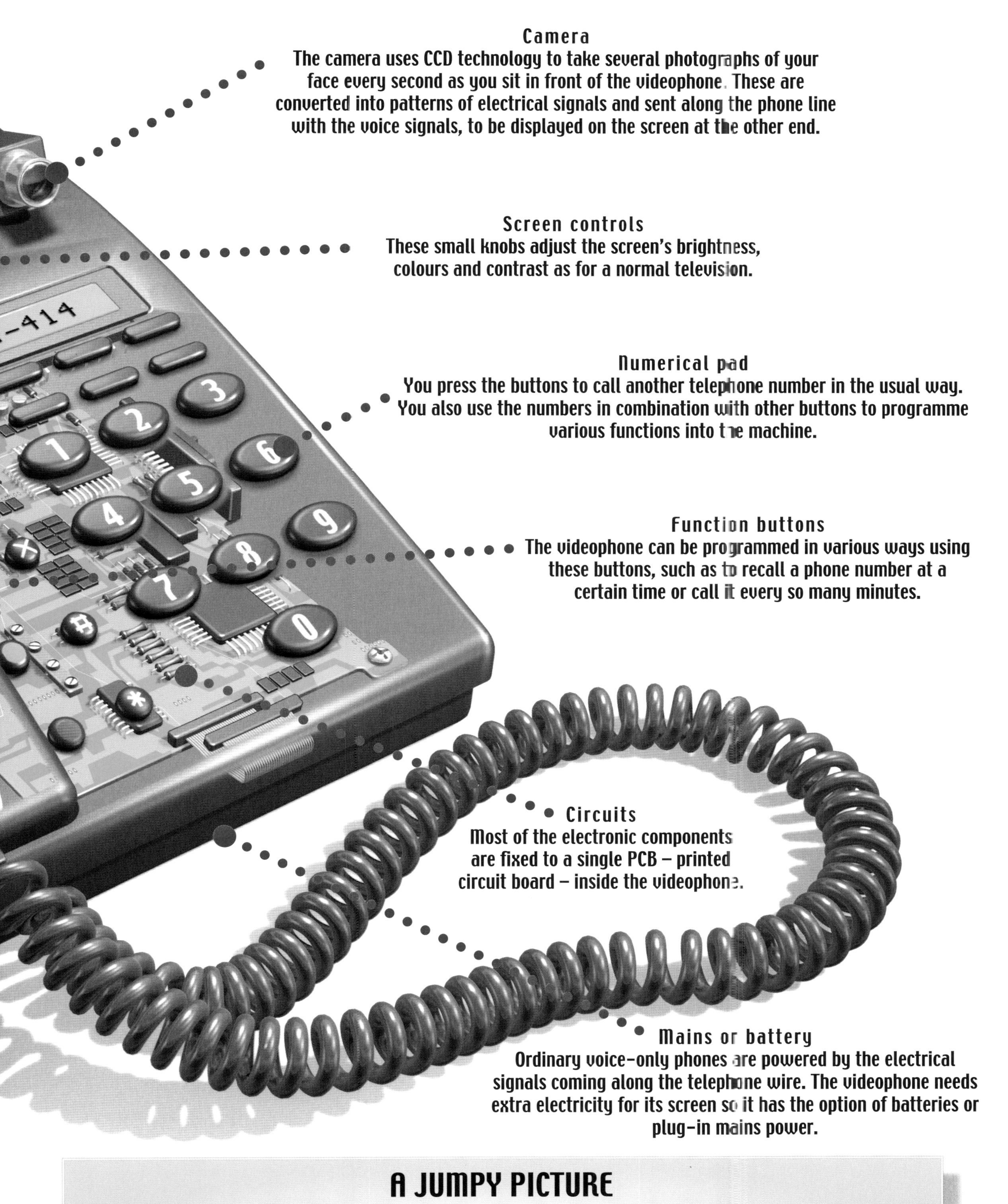

A JUMPY PICTURE

When a full colour picture is converted into electrical signals, even at the small size of the videophone screen shown here, the result is many thousands of signals. If the picture is designed to show movement, this becomes millions of signals per second. Most phone lines are unable to carry this much information. They are designed for the relatively limited number of signals representing the sound of the voice. Because of this limited capacity, only a small colour picture can be sent and this can change only a few times a second, producing a jumping or flickering image.

HI-TECH OFFICE

Ceiling fan-filter
The fan circulates scented air around the office and filters out bits of dust and nasty smells. It also changes the weak amounts of static electricity on the tiny specks floating in air. This 'ionizing' helps some people to feel more energetic and lively, work better and avoid headaches and stress.

Scented wall light
The wall lamp automatically brightens or dims as the outside light levels change. It also gives out scents such as pine, rose, lemon, mint, fresh-baked bread or fresh-ground coffee. These help to put the people in the right type of mood for whatever work they are doing.

Voice control sound system
The music system can be used to play the radio, audio cassettes and audio CDs in the usual way. It is also linked to a voice control programme so you can turn it up or down, switch programmes or link it into the computer network with just a word or two of command.

Flat wall screen
This looks like a flat painting on the wall. But it is a televison screen linked to the music system. It can also become a computer monitor screen. It is hung or propped up almost anywhere, linked into the computers and video systems by the cable-less IR network.

Videophone terminal
When you make a telephone call, you can both hear and see the person at the other end of the line. This screen also shows people outside the door waiting to come in, for security.

Secure door
The door stays locked unless it recognizes your exact voice, fingerprints and eye scan.

Massage seats
The cushioning in the seats gradually ripples, and the angles of the seat base and back slowly change, to gently move the body and massage away aches and pains.

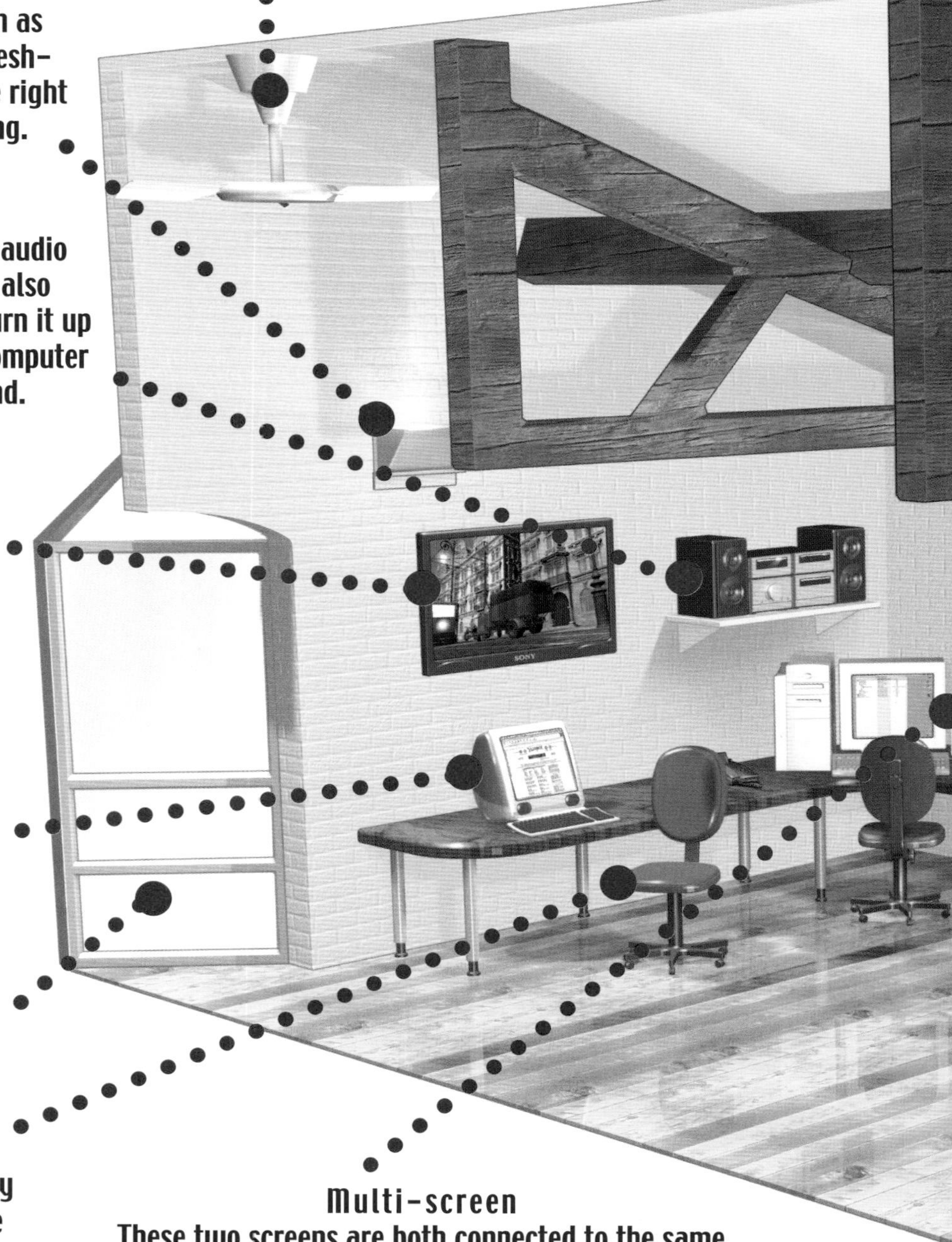

Multi-screen
These two screens are both connected to the same computer. They can show different versions of the same image, one of the broad picture and one in close-up.

CAN YOU EVER KEEP UP?

The speed of development in computers, scanners, printers and other electronic equipment is staggering, even frightening. It's often said that as soon as you take a new computer out of its box, it is out of date. Keeping up with the latest technology can be a costly business.

True, progress is astonishing. But many computers and other machines are 'update-able' or 'forwardly compatible' or 'upgrade-able'. For a few years at least they can have new chips or circuits slotted into them. This will make them work faster, hold more memory and run the newest programs. In this way you do not have to buy a whole new device, just a part for it.

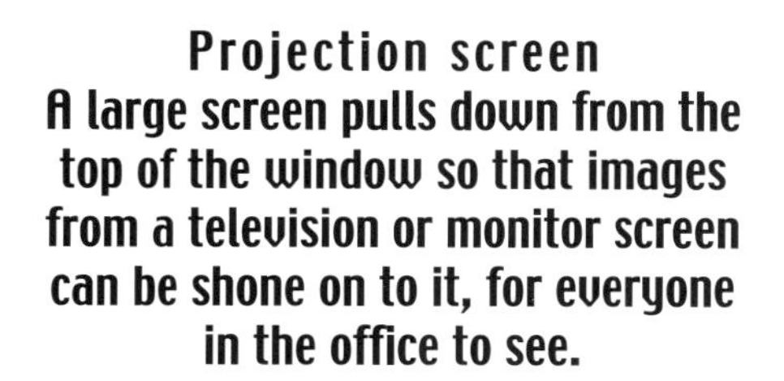

Projection screen
A large screen pulls down from the top of the window so that images from a television or monitor screen can be shone on to it, for everyone in the office to see.

Automatic sun and shade
The window blinds are computer controlled to rise or open when it's cloudy or the sun is not too bright, and to lower or close when the sunshine is too fierce or at night. Coupled with the lighting controls, this maintains the best light levels in the office.

Laptop
This small computer is taken out of the office for meetings elsewhere and for work while travelling or on business trips.

Mood wall
The walls are yellow – at the moment. They are huge light panels that can glow very softly and change colour to match the mood and type of work.

Picture window
The window is clear glass so that you can see outside. But it can also change to show a range of pictures, such as snow-capped mountains, cliffs, fields and hedges or the beach, for a change of scene.

Scanner-printer
This gadget is a combined image scanner and colour printer. It can also be used as a back-up fax-copier if the main one fails. It can print out photographs, too.

Fax-copier
This gadget is a combined colour fax machine and colour photocopier. It can also be used as a back-up scanner-printer if the main one fails. It can print out the day's newspapers, too, after these have been sent in electronic form along the telecom network.

IR cable-less networking
All of the equipment and gadgets in the office are linked by a system of invisible infra-red beams. Also they are all powered by battery packs which plug into the mains once each week for recharging. So any item of equipment can be picked up and moved around without trailing wires and cables.

BOB-WER (BOBW)

This office has BOBW – the 'best of both worlds'. It can be quiet and peaceful with restful colours, dimmed lighting, countryside surroundings and few gadgets and equipment on show. Yet in a few seconds it can be a hive of activity and energy, full of colour and brightness, movement, lively sounds and numerous machines all working away at top speed. This might seem like an extreme example, but it could be the workplace of the future!

MEDICAL SCANNER

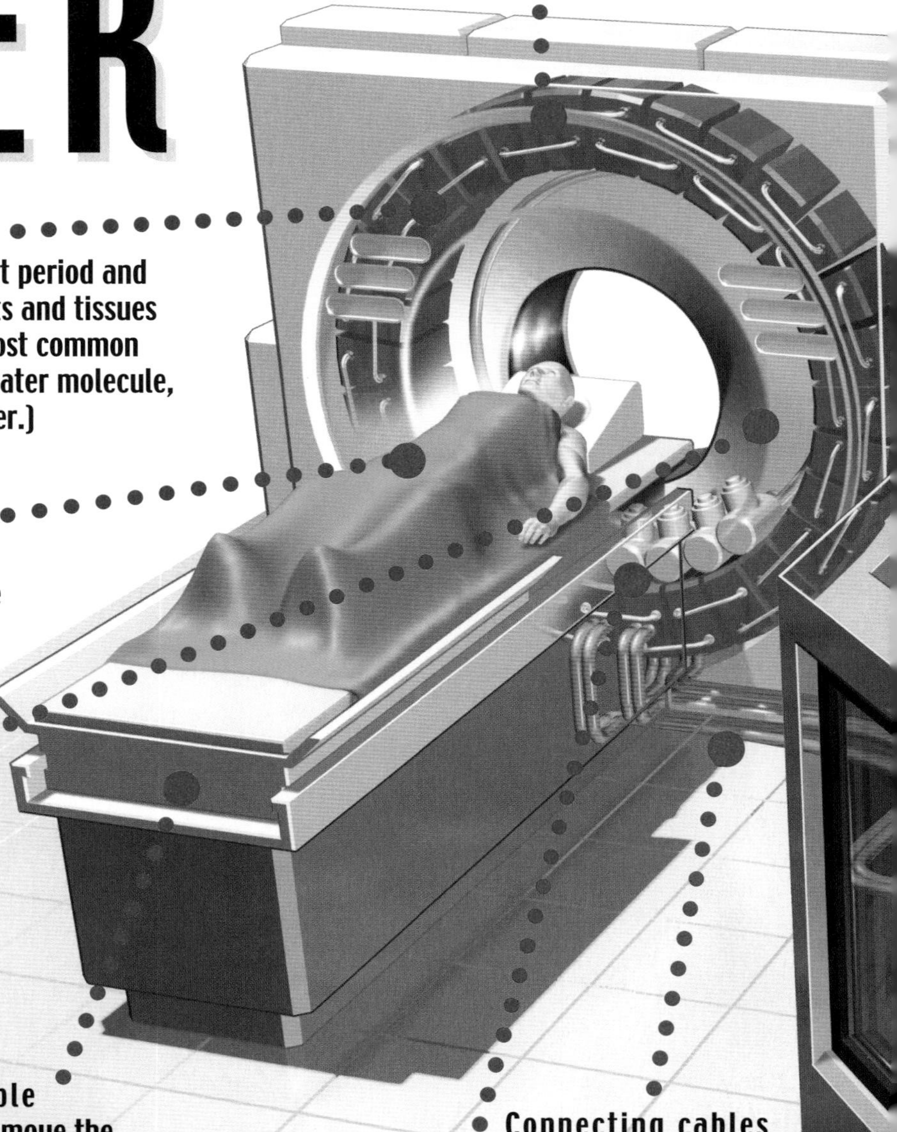

Rotating drum
The drum inside the casing twists so that the magnets and detectors can rotate around the body and scan it from different angles.

Superconducting magnets
Very powerful magnets 'magnetize' the body for a short period and affect the way the billions of hydrogen atoms in its parts and tissues line up and spin around. (Hydrogen, H, is one of the most common chemical elements in the body, making up part of each water molecule, H_2O – and the body is almost two-thirds water.)

Patient
The patient lies still on a bed-like table. He or she may be given a sedative to relax the body and mind and ease any worries. A particular substance or chemical may also be injected into the patient to make certain kinds of scan clearer.

Scanner casing
The working parts of the scanner are contained inside a strong metal case, to protect the people on the outside and the delicate circuits and components inside.

Sliding table
The table slides to move the patient along so that successive horizontal levels or sections of the body can be scanned, one at a time. This builds up a 3-D image.

Connecting cables
Thick cables containing many individual wires link the scanner and control console.

Radio units
Radio waves are beamed through the magnetized body and affect the way the hydrogen atoms line up and spin. As they alter their alignment and spin, the atoms send out their own tiny pulses of radio waves, which are detected by the radio sensors. They form electrical signals, which are sent to the computer along with signals about the angle, strength and timing of the beams.

A Worrying Experience

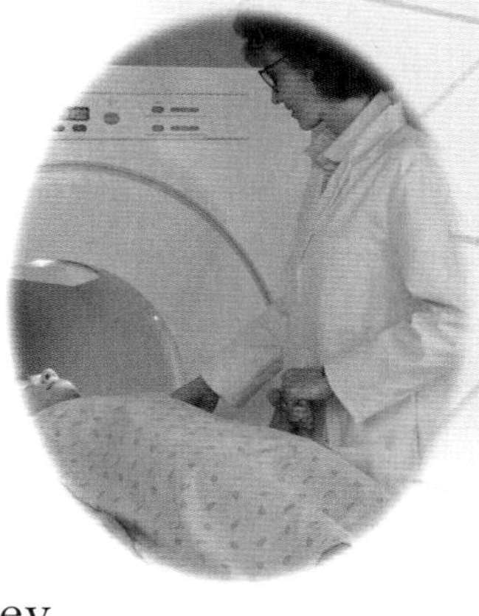

Having a scan can be a worrying process. But it is painless and usually over very quickly. Modern scanning machines are as harmless as they can be made, and there are virtually no risks.

Monitor screen
The scan images are shown on the TV-style computer monitor screens. Different body parts such as nerves, bones and blood have different amounts of brightness or intensity. These can be colour-coded by the computer to make the differences clearer.

Protective screen
A protective wall surrounds the operators and other people and shields them from any harmful effects of the scanning equipment. For an individual patient who is in the room for a short time the risks are almost zero. But they increase for the operators and other staff who are there hour after hour, week after week.

Viewing window
Operators can watch through the window to check all is well with the patient and equipment. The glass is specially strengthened and treated for protection.

Computer
Huge amounts of computer power are needed to decode the signals coming in from the radio sensors and other equipment, analyse them and gradually build up the scan pictures section by section.

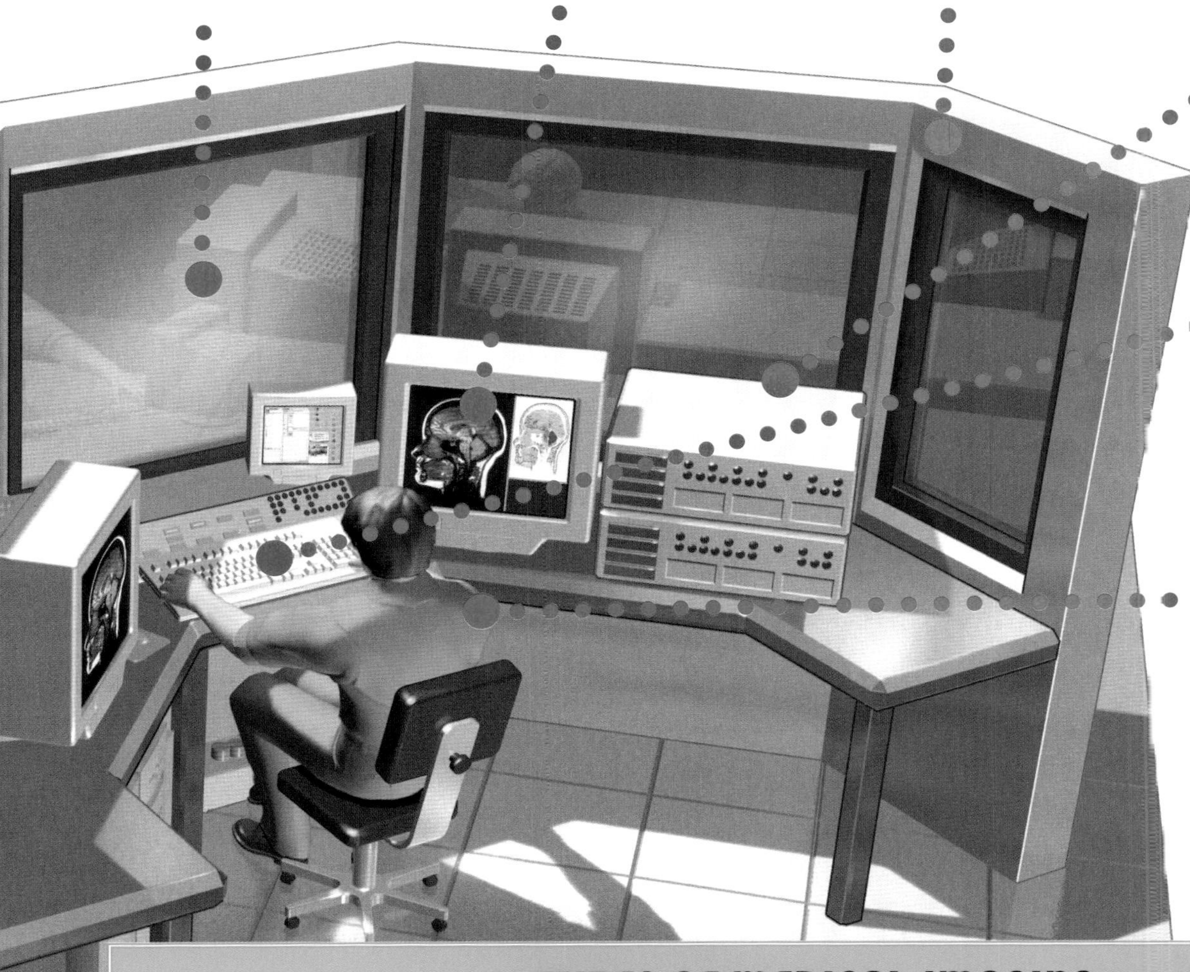

Controls
The operator controls the computer, which controls the scanner and other equipment. Most of the instructions are fed in by typing on to the keyboard as with a normal computer.

Operator
The operator is highly skilled in various areas including medicine, human anatomy (body structure), computer operations and engineering.

TYPES OF MEDICAL IMAGING

There are many ways of looking inside the body without cutting it open:

- X-rays are useful for showing bones and teeth. Modern X-rays are very safe but strong X-rays can harm the body.
- CT (computerized tomography or CAT, computerized axial tomography) uses weak X-rays that are not harmful. It scans the body slice by slice and puts the slices together for a detailed 3-D result.
- An ultrasound scan beams sound waves, too high-pitched for our hearing, into the body and analyses the echoes. It is used to examine babies in the womb.
- The MR (magnetic resonance imaging) scan gets detailed results by putting the body in a powerful magnetic field and beaming radio waves through it.
- PET (positron emission tomography) involves injecting 'tagged' substances into the body, such as hormones or blood sugar. The scanner tracks the substance and shows how it is used. PET scans are often used on the brain.

LIGHT SHOW

Wow!

Lighting displays can be so spectacular at a music show that they distract the audience from the sounds and musicians on stage.

SFX units
There are hundreds of special lighting effects (SFX). This is the stargate effect, where a pool of light seems to form a moving, rippling, glinting area like the surface of a pond.

Motorized mirrors
It takes a very powerful and expensive electric motor to tilt or swivel a whole heavy light unit so that its beam moves about. But a much smaller motor can tilt a mirror that reflects the beam to give the same effect.

Speaker banks
A massive sound system complements the lighting rig for a huge and spectacular show.

LASER LIGHT VERSUS ORDINARY LIGHT

- Laser light is the same type of energy as daylight or electric light. But it has greater intensity and power. A very strong laser beam can cut through solid metal. Almost any laser beam can harm the eyes, so it should never be shone into them.
- Laser light is one colour. The colour of light depends on its wavelength. Ordinary white light has a whole range of wavelengths that we see as all the colours of the rainbow. Light from a laser has just one wavelength so it is a single, pure colour.
- Laser light is coherent. This means its waves are arranged so that their peaks are all in line or in phase. It can travel further without fading.
- Unlike normal light rays, laser light rays don't spread out from their source. A laser beam stays the same width no matter how far it goes.

Sky pencil laser beams
Laser beams shine skywards, staying the same width and colour and brightness for as far as the eye can see. Certain types of laser light cannot be shone down towards the audience in case they harm the eyes.

Lighting gantry
Tall towers or frames on either side support a beam-like framework that runs across the top of the stage. Lights are hung from this gantry.

Spotlights
Bright, narrow beams of ordinary light illuminate small areas or spots.

Filters
White light is made up of all the colours of the rainbow. Coloured filters stop most of the colours from passing through them to leave only the required one such as red or green.

Follow spotlights
These spotlight beams move about to follow the performers as they move, keeping them brightly lit in small pools of light.

Side spotlights
More spotlight beams shine from the sides to illuminate the central area of the stage.

Wash backlights
Large areas of fainter colour are played on the surfaces at the rear of the stage by wash lights. This is much cheaper than painting the stage surfaces and the colour can be changed or turned off at the flick of a switch.

Footlights
Dimmer lights shine up from below. This helps to reduce the shadows under objects such as tables and chins caused by the bright lights from above.

Control computer
A computer system is programmed to switch the various lights on and off, make them dimmer or brighter, flash, change their colours and make the beams move around – all at precise times. This is usually faster and more reliable than having human operators for the lights, except for the follow spotlights.

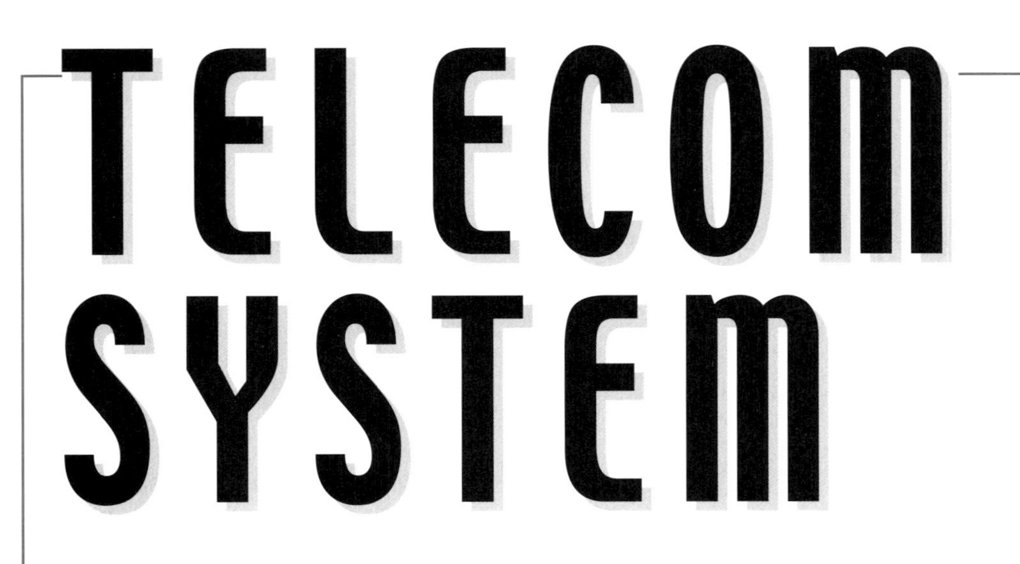

TELECOM SYSTEM

Central exchange
The central exchange handles calls coming in and going out and routes them over a whole city. Or it may serve a wider country region where users are just as numerous but more spread out.

Exchange network
The computers and other equipment inside the exchange are all linked or networked to each other. Non-automatic calls and other information can be routed from one person to another.

Trunk cable
A trunk cable or land line is a major link carrying huge amounts of information or data. Trunk cables or landlines are usually fibre optic. They are bundles of very long but very thin rods of glass, each one thinner than a human hair. Each cable has thousands of fibres and each fibre can carry thousands of telephone calls. The information of the call passes along the fibres at the speed of light. It is not in the form of coded electrical pulses but as pulses of laser light.

SOME TELECOM DEVICES

About 30 years ago almost the only device you could attach to a telephone line was a telephone on its wire. Now the choice of devices includes:

- A cordless telephone. It has a base set attached to the phone line by a wire, and a low-power radio link to the handset so you can walk about nearby while using it.
- An answerphone that plays a pre-recorded message and then records what the caller has to say.
- A fax machine that scans writing, drawing or other marks on paper and turns them into coded signals for the telecom network.
- A computer which is linked to the network by a modem. The modem alters the digital coded signals inside the computer into analogue coded signals suitable for the general telecom system.

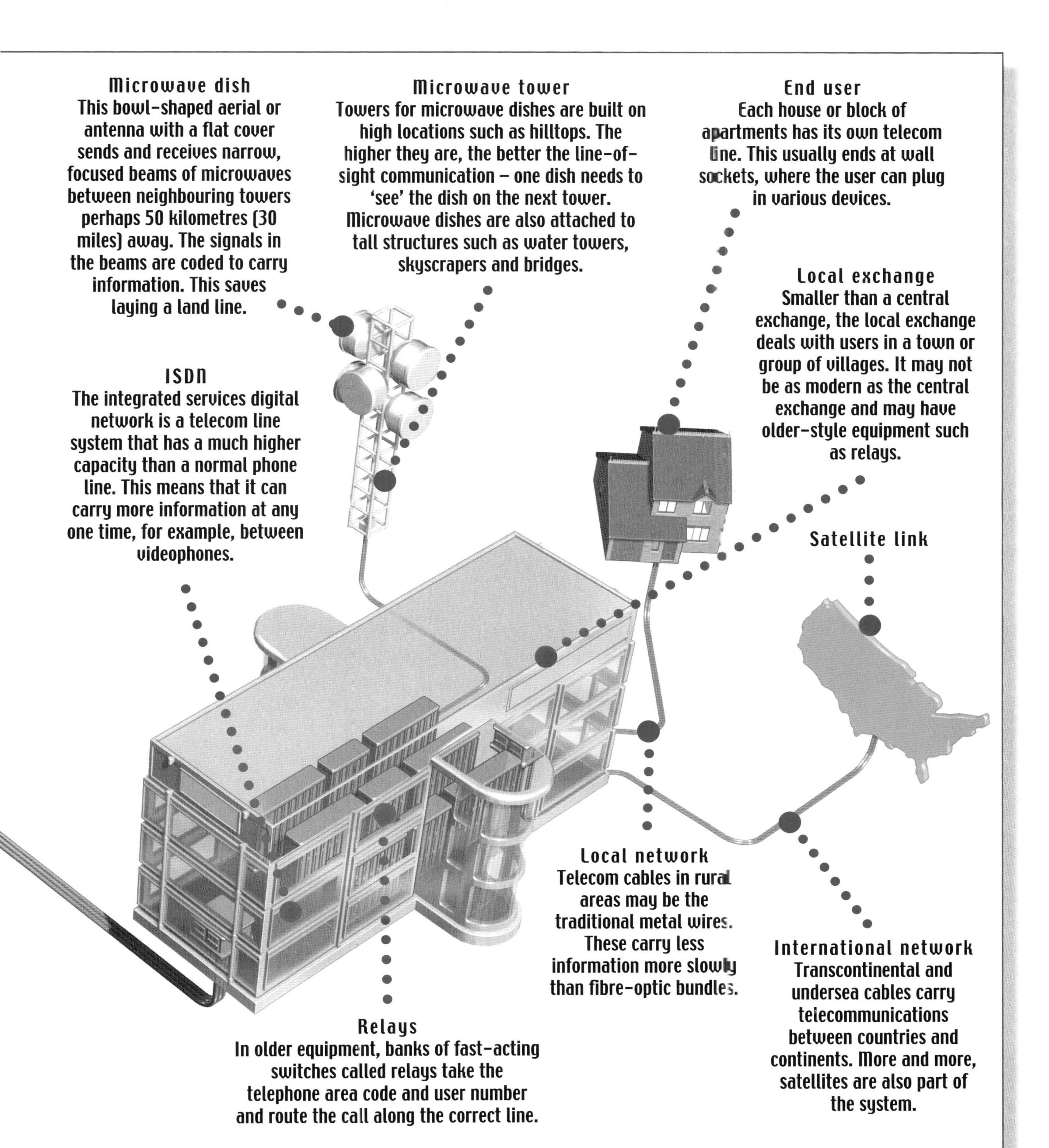

WHAT GOES ALONG THE TELEPHONE LINE?

Information or data. This is in the form of pulses of electricity in a metal wire, flashes of laser light in an optical fibre, or patterns of waves for radio and microwaves. Each way or mode of transmission has its own coding system. The data can represent almost anything from the sound of the human voice to a full orchestra, images and pictures, lists of numbers and calculations, sentences of words and so on. Once they are put into coded form the system deals with all of them in the same way.

SATELLITE TV

Dish
The dish is an antenna or aerial that receives radio signals from the satellite broadcast. It must be pointed at exactly the right angle, both sideways and upwards, to receive the strongest signals from the satellite far above. Satellites that broadcast TV programmes are in a special geostationary orbit (GSO) above the Equator of the Earth. So in the northern parts of the world satellite dishes always point south, and in the south, they point north.

Parabolic mesh
The shape of the dish and its mesh is a parabola or similar curve. This reflects the radio signals and focuses or concentrates them on to the receiver.

Too Many Dishes

Some people complain that satellite dishes are unsightly. Local laws often prevent them being fixed to historic buildings.

Receiver arm
The arm holds the receiver unit at precisely the correct distance and angle from the dish to receive the focused signals.

Offset receiver
Radio signals are detected and turned into electrical signals by the receiver. This is offset, or not in line with the centre of the dish, so it does not get in the way of the incoming radio signals.

SATELLITE, TERRESTRIAL AND CABLE

Signals for television programmes can arrive at a TV set in one of three main ways.

- Satellite: This is DBS, direct broadcast by satellite. The signals are in the form of invisible radio waves that come from a satellite high in space. They are broadcast over a wide area and the individual dishes of users pick them up. As domestic dishes are quite small, the satellite must send out powerful signals. The main area where the signals can be received is called the satellite's 'footprint'.
- Terrestrial: The radio signals are beamed out by antennae on tall towers or high buildings. They can usually be received by an antenna shaped like a long bar with cross-pieces.
- Cable: The signals are sent as coded pulses of laser light flashing along a fibre-optic cable buried underground. This system is often combined with telephone and computer lines which work in the same way.

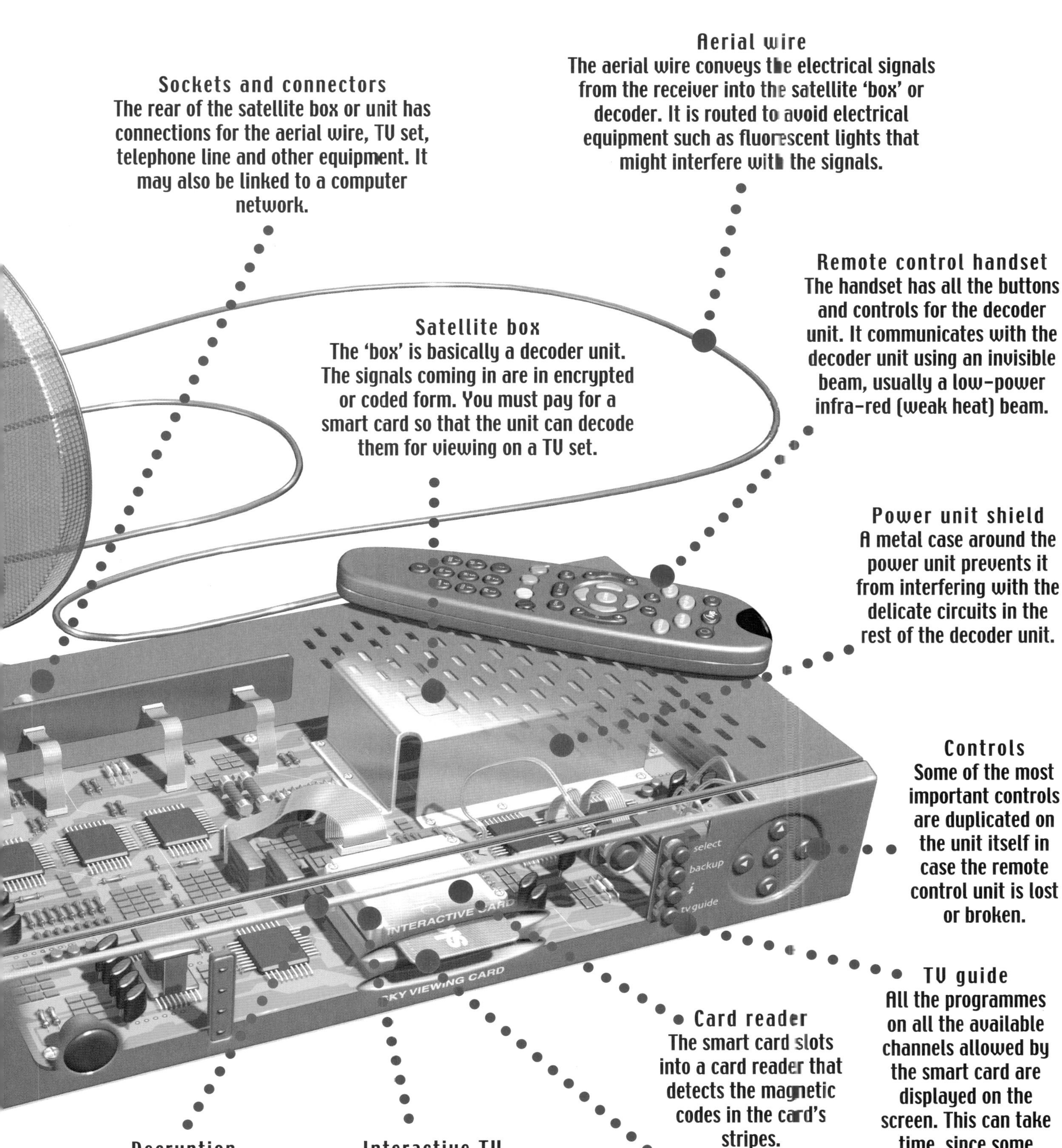

Sockets and connectors
The rear of the satellite box or unit has connections for the aerial wire, TV set, telephone line and other equipment. It may also be linked to a computer network.

Aerial wire
The aerial wire conveys the electrical signals from the receiver into the satellite 'box' or decoder. It is routed to avoid electrical equipment such as fluorescent lights that might interfere with the signals.

Remote control handset
The handset has all the buttons and controls for the decoder unit. It communicates with the decoder unit using an invisible beam, usually a low-power infra-red (weak heat) beam.

Satellite box
The 'box' is basically a decoder unit. The signals coming in are in encrypted or coded form. You must pay for a smart card so that the unit can decode them for viewing on a TV set.

Power unit shield
A metal case around the power unit prevents it from interfering with the delicate circuits in the rest of the decoder unit.

Controls
Some of the most important controls are duplicated on the unit itself in case the remote control unit is lost or broken.

TV guide
All the programmes on all the available channels allowed by the smart card are displayed on the screen. This can take time, since some satellite systems have more than 100 channels.

Card reader
The smart card slots into a card reader that detects the magnetic codes in the card's stripes.

Decryption
The signals coming in from the satellite broadcast are encrypted, or 'scrambled'. The method of encryption changes regularly. Only if the smart card is suited for the date and channel, will the decryption unit un-scramble or decode the signals so they can be fed into the TV set.

Interactive TV
Some decoder units are interactive, that is, they can send as well as receive. The user receives information via the satellite broadcast, for example, from a shopping channel. He or she then uses the handset to send information from the unit via a connection to the phone line, to order goods.

Smart card
The card has various code numbers represented by tiny patches of magnetism in its stripes. These include the dates and channels that have been paid for. They are matched to the broadcast information coming in with the pictures and sound. If the card is out of date or the channel is not on the accepted list, the unit stops its signals.

INTERNET

LOGGING ON TO THE NET

The Internet is the worldwide international network of interlinked computers and other electronic devices. It is not really one single network but complex groups of smaller networks joined together. You need a computer that plugs into the phone line or telecom system to use it. You 'log on' by sending signals to your ISP, Internet service provider. The ISP's own computer acts as a go-between or intermediate between your computer and the whole network. You 'download' by receiving along the phone line the electrical signals that represent various forms of information such as words, pictures, sounds and computer programs, and storing these in your computer.

Global telecom network
The telecommunications network involves telephone exchanges, computers of all shapes and sizes, fax machines, landlines, microwave and satellite links and many other parts.

E-mail
'E' or electronic mail does not use paper. You type or make a message on your computer, address it to the recipient and send it along the telephone line to your e-mail provider. The message waits there, stored on what is effectively a huge computer disc, until the recipient uses his or her computer to call up and collect it.

Modem link
The modem is a device that changes the tiny digital electronic pulses inside the computer into electrical signals suitable for feeding into the telecom network.

Back/Forwards
Clicking on these arrows goes to the previous page you were looking at on the screen, or to the next page on the list.

Address
The address is not a physical place like a house or office. It is an electronic label for a certain website or e-mail recipient – more like the address of their computer.

Option panels or buttons
You can choose what to see next by using the mouse to position the computer's cursor or arrow on one of these panels or 'screen buttons' and then clicking the mouse.

Mouse

THE WEB

Imagine a vast library of books, pictures, movies, adverts, music, catalogues and other works and publications. The World Wide Web is like this but in electronic form. It exists as tiny electrical signals inside computers and whizzing along telephone lines. You can look up a website, which is like taking a library book or catalogue off the shelf. This is usually made by one company or organization and it is about a certain subject. You can look at the different pages on screen just as you would flick through the book. But using the Web is far quicker than visiting a library. Web sites can be continents away. They can be changed and updated at any time. Unlike a book, they are two-way – you can send information, messages, orders and money to them as well as receiving goods or information from them.

Destination computer
The message from your computer can reach another computer on the opposite side of the world in just one second. However, the various delays and changes as it passes through the system mean that the transfer time is usually slightly longer.

Search engine
You can search the Net using a search engine. This is a computer program or application that scans the network for the key words or phrases that you enter, and shows you a list of possible addresses that might be helpful. You can search in a certain country, a continent or across the whole world.

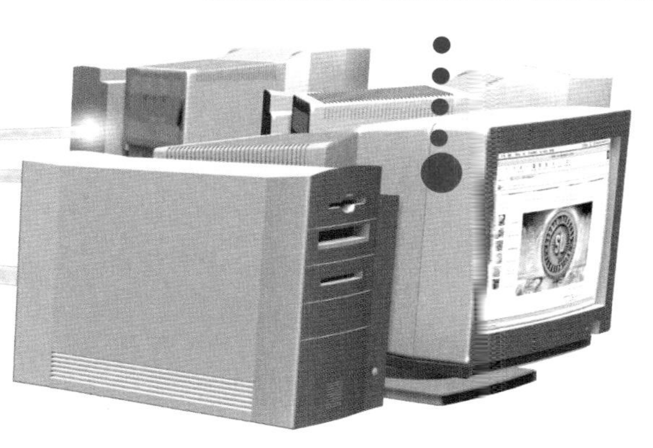

Hub
A hub is a concentrated centre where many big computers send and receive information rapidly. Gateway computers change information or data into the different forms and codes, called protocols, used in various countries.

ISP or Server

Screen and page
A page may be more than just what you can see on your screen. You may have to move or scroll the page sideways or down so you can see the rest of it as it comes on to the screen. It's like moving the large page of a newspaper or magazine around behind a smaller opening, which is the screen.

Image
Pictures tend to download (arrive in your computer) more slowly than words. They can be copied into the memory of your own computer, but they take up much more memory space than words.

Text
Words usually download, or come into your computer, very quickly. You can highlight or choose them, copy them into your own computer's memory, then store them in one of your own files or documents.

User's computer

SATELLITE NAVIGATION SYSTEM

Comsat
A communications satellite is part of the worldwide telecom network. It receives and sends on radio signals for telephone calls, TV programmes, computer messages and many other forms of long-distance communication.

Dish antenna
The large dish can send and receive faint or faraway signals. It can be moved by electric motors and pointed very precisely at a certain satellite, and moved to link with other satellites at different times.

Ground station
This is in communication with many satellites via its large dish and other aerials. It also contacts other stations on the ground by terrestrial radio and microwave links, and by the cables and landlines of the telecom network.

Ship to shore
Direct radio links between a ship and land can only be carried out over limited distances. Too far away and the curve of the Earth's surface gets in the way, since most radio signals go in straight lines and not around bends. This is why satellites are so useful. They can receive signals on the uplink and then beam them down somewhere else a continent away. They act like relay or passing-on radio sets on incredibly tall towers.

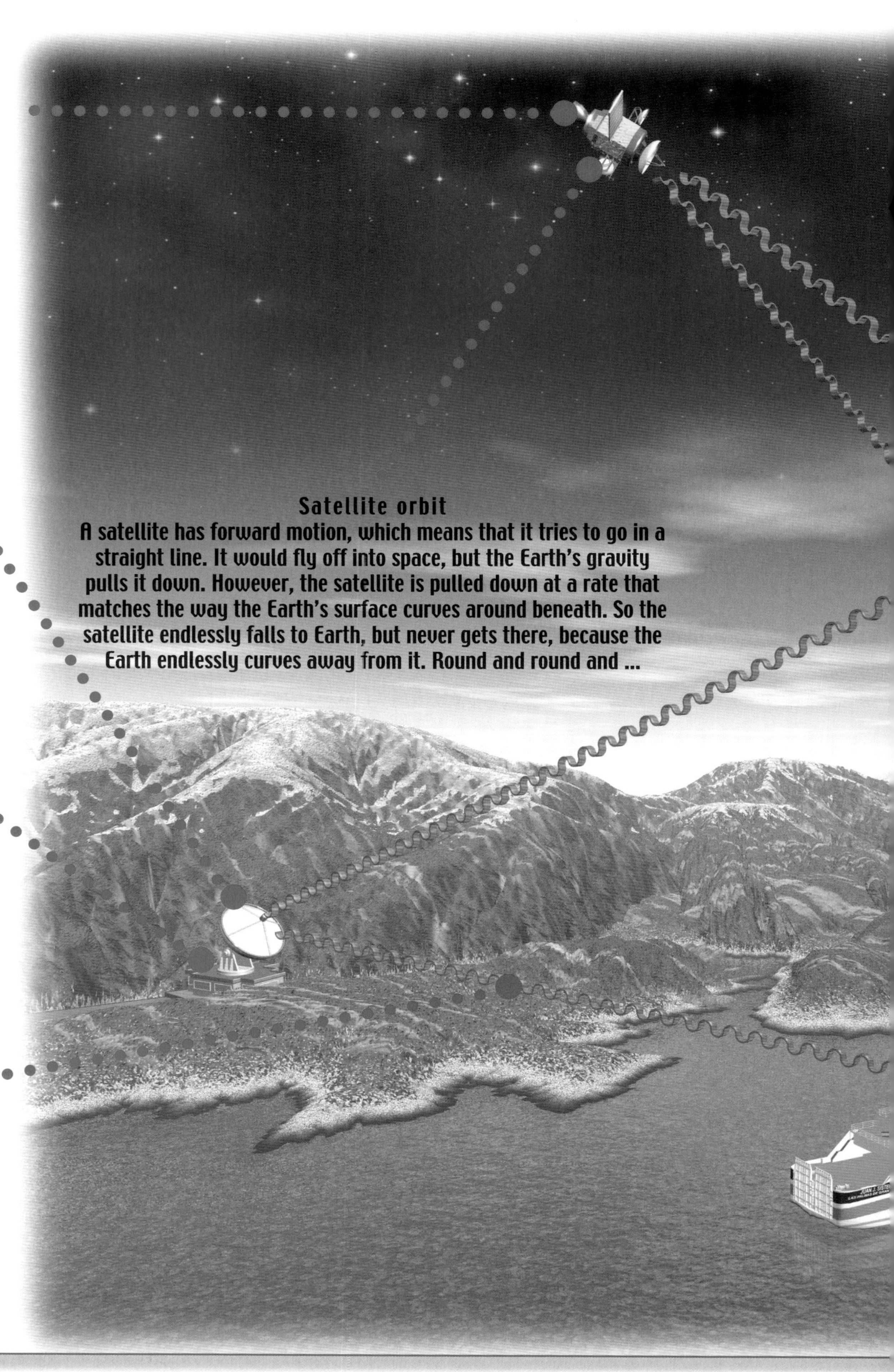

Satellite orbit
A satellite has forward motion, which means that it tries to go in a straight line. It would fly off into space, but the Earth's gravity pulls it down. However, the satellite is pulled down at a rate that matches the way the Earth's surface curves around beneath. So the satellite endlessly falls to Earth, but never gets there, because the Earth endlessly curves away from it. Round and round and ...

THE SPEED OF LIGHT

Radio and microwave signals go up and down to satellites at the fastest possible speed, the speed of light. This is about 300,000 kilometres per second (186,000 miles per second). However, some satellites are so far away that signals take more than one-tenth of a second to get there. If the signals go up and down to several satellites on their journey around the globe, the delay can add up to almost a second!

GSO

Most satellites seem to move across the sky when seen from down here on Earth. But a satellite 35,787 kilometres (about 22,000 miles) directly above the Equator has an orbit speed that means it goes once around the Earth in 24 hours. The Earth itself spins around once in the same time. So looking up from the surface of Earth, the satellite seems to hover or hang in the same place all the time. This orbit is called a geostationary or geosynchronous orbit, GSO. It means that dish aerials do not have to move or tilt to track the satellite across the sky. They can be left pointing in one direction at it. GSO is used for several types of satellite, especially those which broadcast satellite TV programmes into our homes.

SARSAT

Many ships, planes and vehicles carry a SARSAT radio beacon or transmitter. In case of trouble or emergency this sends out radio signals on an emergency channel. The signals are picked up by a world system of SARSATs, Search And Rescue SATellites. The SARSATs send alert signals down to ground stations. The time delay for the radio signals from the emergency transmitter reaching the various SARSATs in their different positions gives the location of the transmitter, and so the search and rescue can begin.

Navigation beacon

A lighthouse sends out pulses of light. The length and pattern of the pulses is a code for the identity of the lighthouse. In the same way a radio beacon sends out radio signals for its own identity or 'name', showing ships that it is nearby. The time delay between the radio signals from several beacons allows you to work out your own position in relation to them.

FUTURE GADGETS

The last few years of the twentieth century saw an astonishing increase in the numbers of gadgets. Three in particular made their mark – the mobile phone, the hand-held satellite navigation (GPS) receiver, and the MP3 solid-state digital music player. The mother of all gadgets, the computer, came into many homes. The numbers of people logging on to the Internet more than doubled each year. Never before have so many types of gadgetry taken the world by storm in this way.

BUILT TO LAST?

What will happen in this century? There are bound to be more new gadgets. We will not even know that we need some of them until they are invented. Then, like the mobile phone, they could work their way into our daily lives and become almost indispensable. Others could come and go with changing fashions.

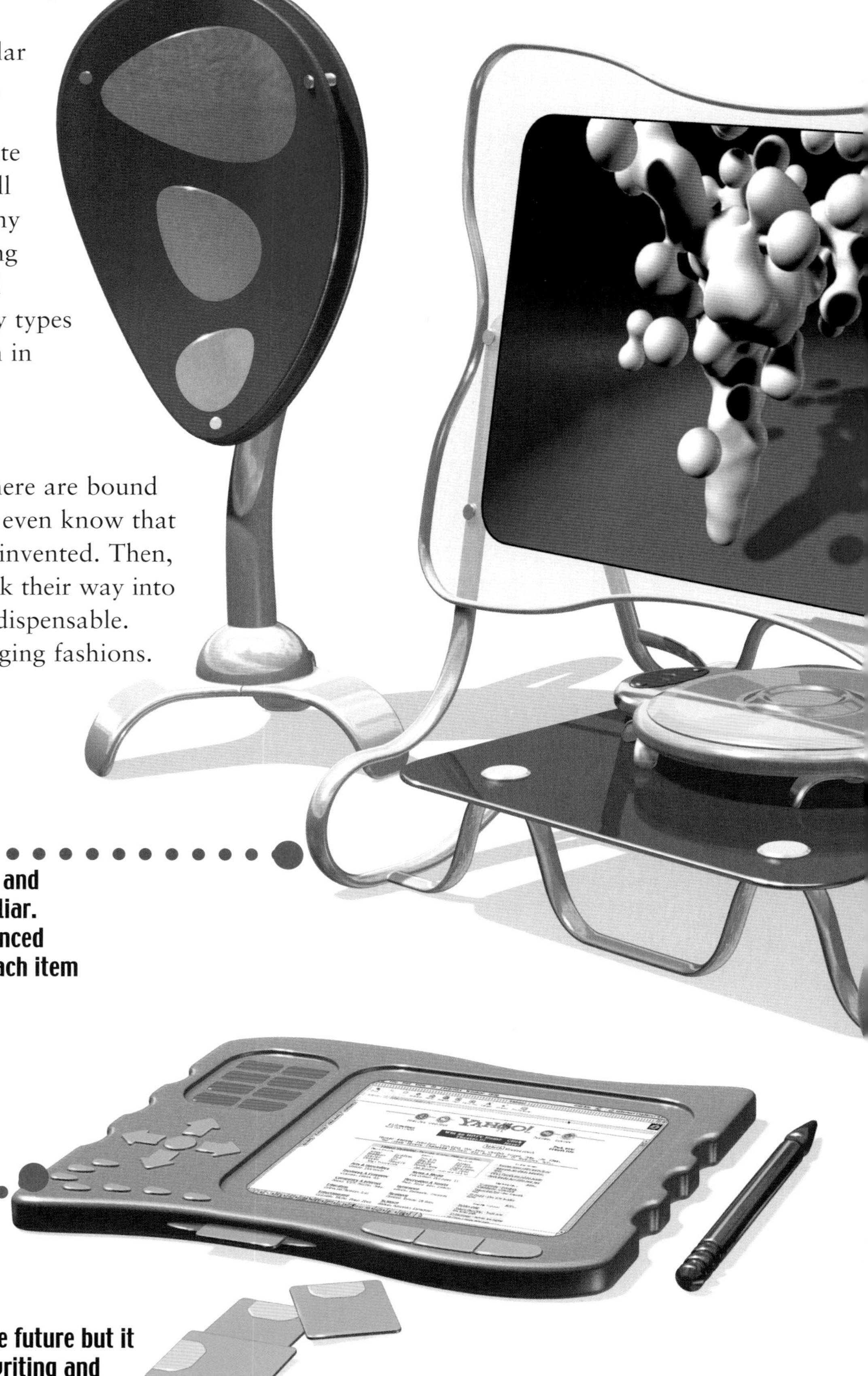

GADGETS ON THE TABLE
This tabletop of electronic devices and equipment may look vaguely familiar. They seem like slightly more advanced versions of today's gadgets. But each item has a surprise in store...

PEN AND PAD
The electronic notepad is still around in the future but it does far more that understand your handwriting and store the addresses of friends. It is linked to the satellite navigation system and displays your exact position on a map. It shows TV channels and videos. Its diary reminds you of appointments and meetings. It has a tiny camera and microphone and works as a videophone so you can talk face-to-face with others.

3-D SCREEN
The screen is holographic. It gives a 3-D image. As you move to the side (detected by the motion sensor earpiece) you can see around and behind objects in the foreground. The screen also zooms in and out by voice control so you can see the whole scene, or look at just a small part in greatly enlarged close-up.

MUSIC AND MOOD
The speakers give out sounds and music but they are also mood generators. They produce a combination of vibrations, scents, biological chemicals called pheromones, lights, and sounds that are too high (ultrasonic) or low (infrasonic) for the ears. You cannot hear them but they affect the body in other ways. This can put you into any kind of mood or feeling you wish.

PERSONAL COMMUNICATIONS

One trend could be for the gadgets we have today to become smaller, simpler and combined together. Interactive TV and Internet computing could merge to give the full range of hundreds of channels for shopping, entertainment, business and research. In 10 or 20 years everyone might have a hand-held device that looks like a miniature TV, but is also a video recorder, a mobile phone, a voice-operated computer linked into the Internet, a radio and music player all in one small box. It's the total personal communications gadget.

NEW DIRECTIONS

Gadgets could also take us into whole new areas that we can only dream about. Our TV and monitor screens show images that are flat, in two dimensions. What about a 3-D version using hologram technology? In the corner of your room you could have a hologram TV of your favourite sports team playing for the world championship, as tiny animated models made of light.

THE WORLD ON YOUR WRIST
The wristwatch is the tiny monitor screen of a computer that is radio-linked to the Internet. It has no buttons. It is operated by your voice or by your hand and finger movements which it detects through the strap. It is also radio-linked to the earpiece so you can hear speech, music and other sounds. Oh, and it tells the time too.

THINKING AHEAD

Voice control is fine, but why not thought control? Maybe we will be able to communicate directly with our computers by holding a sensor to the head that detects our brain waves. Ideas, thoughts, memories, moods and emotions could flow between the living brain and the electronic one. In the end, where will human beings finish and electronic gadgets begin?

GLOSSARY

analogue A device that works by electricity or another form of energy which varies in a continuous way, like waves rippling up and down, rather than in a step-wise way (see digital).

antenna An aerial, detector or sensor, usually for radio waves or microwaves.

binary Counting with only two numbers, usually written as 0 (zero) and 1 (one).

capstan A rod, pole, drum or similar shape that turns around to wind in a cable or move something along.

cathode In electrical equipment, a disc or rod or plate which is connected to the negative (rather than positive) of the electricity supply.

cathode ray tube (CRT) A shaped glass tube with no air inside, along which beams and particles pass, driven by high-power electricity. The main 'rays' come from the negative end or cathode. They were once called cathode rays but they are really beams of particles called electrons. Certain types of CRTs were developed into televisions. The main part of a television or monitor is still called a 'tube'.

CCD Charge-coupled device. An electronic 'chip', which detects patterns of light rays that shine on it and produces a corresponding pattern of tiny electrical signals.

CPU Central processing unit. The 'brain' of a computer where all the vital altering, changing, processing and manipulating of the tiny electrical pulses take place.

DBS Direct broadcast by satellite. When a satellite beams out radio waves for radio and TV programmes over a wide area, which can be received by individual users in their homes, offices and factories.

digital A device that works by electricity or another form of energy which varies in a step-wise way, with the steps representing numbers (digits). This differs from analogue where it varies in a continuous way, like waves rippling up and down.

fibre optic Very thin and flexible strands or fibres of special glass or plastic that work optically – by light. They carry pulses of light inside.

FST Flatter squarer tube. A television or monitor screen which has a flatter (less domed) surface and squarer (less rounded) sides and corners. This reduces the distortion or bending of the picture.

GSO Geostationary orbit. When a satellite goes around or orbits the Earth exactly once each day. The Earth spins around exactly once each day, too.

helical A line or shape that goes around in a circle and also along, like a corkscrew or the thread (raised ridge) of a bolt.

ISDN Integrated services digital network. A method of connecting computers, scanners, printers, cameras, telephones and other equipment so they all work digitally.

LCD Liquid crystal display. A screen or similar kind of display or readout that uses crystals which can change the way light passes through them.

magnetron A device that uses an electric current which changes direction to and fro very fast (oscillates) to produce microwaves.

megaHertz (mHz) One million Hertz. A Hertz is a measure of frequency, which is the number of vibrations, to-and-fro movements or up-and-down waves each second.

megabyte (MB) One million bytes, that is, one million pieces of computer data.

microchip A very thin slice or 'chip' of the substance silicon with thousands or millions of microscopic electronic components on it. Each chip does a certain job like hold memory for a computer or carry out the computer's main processing.

MP3 A music gadget that records, stores and plays back music or other sounds in digital form. It can be connected directly to a computer and the Internet.

MRI Magnetic resonance imaging, a way of making pictures of the inside of the body using very strong magnetism and weak radio waves.

parabola A certain shape of curve often used for a dish or bowl antenna which picks up radio waves.

PCB Printed circuit board, a flat board made with metal tracks or 'wires' already built into it for connecting up electrical components.

pixel A single group of glowing dots on the screen of a television or monitor, which can be controlled in brightness and colour.

platen A flat plate or platform, especially in printing and photocopying machines.

PPT Personal powered transport. A small craft or vehicle with a motor or engine designed mainly for one person.

preamp A pre-amplifier, an electrical device that changes or alters electrical signals before they are made stronger in the main amplifier.

RAM Random access memory. The temporary working memory of a computer which stores the information for a particular task. When the computer is switched off the contents of the RAM are usually lost.

SFX A short way of writing 'special effects'. These are sounds, lights or pictures that are unreal tricks – they cannot be made by real, everyday processes.

subsound Sounds which are so deep or low that they are not so much heard by the ears as felt by the body as it shakes, such as the rumble of thunder.

terrestrial In television, programmes which are broadcast as radio waves from towers or antennae on the ground, rather than from satellites in space or along cables under the ground.

torque Turning or twisting force.

transformer An electrical device that changes the voltage (pushing strength) of electricity.

tweeter A small type of loudspeaker designed to give out mainly high or shrill sounds.

voltage The force or pushing strength of electricity.

wavelength The length of one wave, for example, from one peak to the next. All kinds of waves can be measured in this way.

woofer A large type of loudspeaker designed to give out mainly low or deep sounds.

INDEX

THE COMPLETE STORY OF
PINOCCHIO
AND OTHER TALES

THE COMPLETE STORY OF
PINOCCHIO
AND OTHER TALES

HAMLYN

CONTENTS

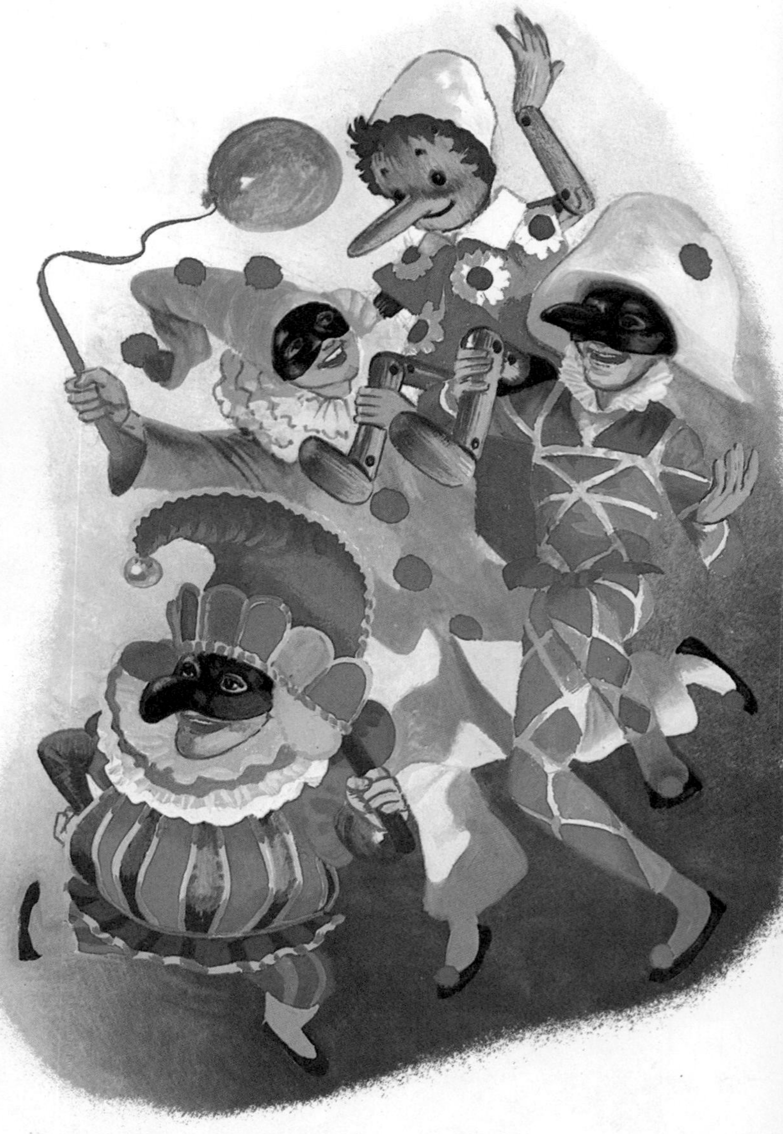

Cover illustration by Francis Phillipps

Cover design by Kasa and Steel

Published 1987 by Hamlyn Publishing
a division of The Hamlyn Publishing Group Limited
Bridge House, London Road,
Twickenham, Middlesex, England

All the material in this compilation was originally published in *Storyteller.*

Produced by Marshall Cavendish Limited

ISBN 0 600 53107 4

Printed and bound in Vicenza, Italy by L.E.G.O.

In Italy, about a hundred years ago, there lived a wood-carver named Geppetto. He was a very poor man, and he lived on his own. Although Geppetto had friendly neighbours, he was lonely at heart and he wished he had a son.

One day he had an idea. He decided to make himself a wooden puppet — a wonderful puppet that would know how to dance and fight and leap like an acrobat. With this puppet, Geppetto could travel the world. People everywhere would pay a lot to see them perform their tricks. But, more important, it would be like a son to him and keep him company.

Straight away, Geppetto chose a log from his wood pile, took his sharpest axe and set to work. But just as he aimed his first blow, he heard a very small voice. "Don't hit me too hard, please!"

You can imagine how surprised the old man was. He looked at the log, he looked all round the room — he even opened the door and looked outside. But he could see no-one. So he started again, just a little more carefully.

All went well as Geppetto stripped off the bark. But when he took his plane to smooth and polish the wood, he heard the same voice breaking out in giggles, "Stop it. Oh, stop it! You're tickling me!" And Geppetto dropped his plane as if he had been struck by a bolt of lightning.

The wood-carver sank into his rickety chair and stared blankly at the piece of wood. He stared and he stared, until it seemed he had been gazing for hours. He scratched his head and he rubbed his chin. He crossed his legs and drummed his fingers on the table. He puffed at his pipe. Then he knocked out the ash and grabbed the log again.

"Well, this couldn't be better," he said to himself at last. "Here I am, making a puppet, and before I have even carved his head, he's talking! By the time I've finished him, he'll be able to walk and run and dance and sing!"

So he chiselled away merrily. Geppetto whistled as he worked, and thought up a name for his puppet. "I'll call him Pinocchio," he decided. "It's a good name — it will bring him luck."

First Geppetto made the head, then he shaped the the forehead, then the eyes, and then the nose. It was there that things started going strangely wrong. The nose began to grow! And it grew and grew and

grew. Poor Geppetto tired himself out chopping the nose down to size.

As for the mouth, it started laughing at Geppetto before it was even finished, and then stuck out a tongue at him as far as it would go!

Geppetto was alarmed, but he pretended not to notice. He pressed on with his work, and fashioned the puppet's body and arms. Then no sooner had he cut out the hands than they pulled his moustache.

"Stop him! Stop him! shouted Geppetto, as he rushed after Pinocchio. But the people were so amazed to see a wooden puppet running down the street that they could hardly move for laughing. The local policeman had more sense. He stepped out into the street and when the puppet tried to dash between his legs he picked him up by his nose.

Poor Geppetto felt more miserable than he had ever felt in his life. What sort of a son was he making for himself? "You young scamp! You're not even finished and already you're being rude to your father! That is bad, very bad." And he wiped a tear from his eye.

There was worse to come. As soon as Geppetto finished off the puppet's legs and feet, Pinocchio gave him a kick on the chin, sprang down to the floor and ran out of the door and away along the street.

Geppetto was grumbling furiously when he reached them. He seized Pinocchio by the neck and hauled him off down the road. "You just wait till we get home. I'll soon show you what happens to naughty boys."

Pinocchio wriggled free and threw himself to the ground, sobbing pathetically. Before Geppetto knew what was happening, all the people were calling to the policeman. "Protect the poor puppet, or Geppetto will kill him!" And they set up such a storm of protest that Geppetto was arrested and locked up in the police station for the night.

Well, Pinocchio was free as a bird, and he scampered off, dancing and leaping and clicking his heels together. He played for hours in the streets and went back home when the sun was setting. He pushed the door open, and threw himself down in Geppetto's old chair by the fireside. Outside, darkness was falling, and it was turning windy and cold, but Pinocchio sat grinning with pleasure. He was warm and cosy — and on the very first day of his life he was his own master.

But Pinocchio was not alone in the room. As he lay back in the chair and closed his eyes, he heard a rapid clicking noise, like the teeth of a comb being scraped on a table's edge, "Cri-cri-cri-cri-cri."

"Who's there?" said Pinocchio.

"It is I." Pinocchio turned round and saw a big insect crawling slowly along the wall. "I am the Talking Cricket, and I have lived in this room for a hundred years and more."

"So what! It's my room now, so just buzz off and leave me alone."

"I will not go until I have told you a great truth," replied the cricket. "Boys who rebel against their parents never come to any good in the world, and sooner or later they will be bitterly sorry for what they have done."

This was the last thing Pinocchio wanted to hear. "Hold your tongue, you silly croaker. Go away."

But the cricket took no notice. "Poor Pinocchio, I pity you. You really *do* have a wooden head, and what is more you will come to a bad end."

At these words, Pinocchio lost his temper. He snatched Geppetto's mallet from the work-bench and hurled it at the cricket. Maybe he didn't mean to hurt him, but the mallet hit the little creature right on the head and he scarcely had time to cry out before he fell limply to the ground. "That's shut you up," said Pinocchio, and he tried to go to sleep.

It was the start of a miserable night for the wicked puppet. No sooner had Pinocchio closed his eyes than he began to feel hungry, so he looked around for something to eat. He hunted high and low, but he could not find a scrap of food.

Just as he was giving up, he spotted an egg lying in a pile of wood shavings. He eagerly cracked it open over a pan — and a tiny chicken popped out, ruffled its feathers twice and flew out of the window! Pinocchio was aching with hunger. He ran out into the streets and searched everywhere for food, but there was nothing to be found.

floor, he felt very sorry for him, and gave his son the three pears he had bought for his own breakfast. Then he placed him gently on the work-bench, and lovingly carved him a new pair of feet. After they were finished, the old wood-carver cut out a special set of clothes for Pinocchio: a pair of short trousers, a colourful shirt of flowered paper, and a cap made from a crust of bread.

In desperation, he rang on a neighbour's doorbell to beg for a meal. But a crotchety old man, angry at being disturbed in the middle of the night, poured a great basin of water all over him.

Pinocchio slunk home like a drowned rat, so cold and exhausted that he flopped down in the chair with his feet in the hearth. For the rest of the night he slept and snored — and all the time his wooden feet were in the fire. Little by little they burned away to cinders. By the morning he could not even stand up.

Geppetto came back from the gaol fuming with anger. But when he saw poor Pinocchio, crawling around on the

Pinocchio was so relieved to be able to walk again, and so excited with his new clothes, that he leapt up from the work-bench, threw his arms around Geppetto's neck, and kissed him again and again. "Oh please help me, Daddy," he sobbed, and he poured out the story of the cricket's warning. "Don't let me come to a bad end — I do *want* to be good."

They hugged each other for a long time. Finally Geppetto spoke through his tears. "If you *really* want to be a good boy, Pinocchio, you must go to school and work hard."

"Oh I will," cried Pinocchio. "I will! I promise I will."

The Puppet Theatre

Pinocchio had promised Geppetto he would be a good puppet and go to school. But first he needed a spelling book, and the wood-carver was so poor that he had no money to by one. Geppetto pulled out his pockets one by one. Then looked in the rusty old tin on his work-bench. But there was not a penny anywhere. With a deep sigh, he put on his coat and went to the door. "Wait for me here, Pinocchio," he said, and disappeared round the corner.

A few minutes later he was back with a spelling book — but without his coat. He had sold it in exchange of the book.

Pinocchio kissed his father again, and thanked him. Then he hurried off to school.

As Pinocchio marched along, all sorts of grand ideas ran through his head.

"Today I shall learn to read," he said to himself, "then tomorrow I'll learn writing, and the next day arithmetic. Then I'll earn lots of money and buy my dear father a beautiful new coat." There was no end to his good intentions — until he heard the sound of drums and trumpets in the distance.

The music was coming from a brightly painted building, and a large sign announced *Puppet Theatre*. At the entrance stood a man beating a drum to announce the start of a performance, and crowds of people were pushing their way into the hall.

Pinocchio could not wait to join them. "How much does it cost to go in?" he asked. "Only two pence to a young lad like you," replied the man outside.

Within seconds Pinocchio had sold the schoolbook to a street trader , bought a ticket and dashed into the theatre.

Imagine his delight when he saw the actors! There were Harlequin and Punch, quarrelling as usual and whacking each other with big sticks. The audience was roaring with laughter. Then Punch caught sight of Pinocchio and there was almost a riot. "It's our little wooden brother," he shouted. "Come up here and join us!" And all the other puppets rushed on to the stage to greet Pinocchio.

What a sight it was! They hugged him and kissed him, gave him friendly pats and pinches, and ended up carrying him in triumph across the stage.

But the audience was not amused. They set up a tremendous racket. *"We want the play! We want the play!"*

Fire-Eater looked hard at Pinocchio, and he suddenly sneezed. It was a sure sign that his pity had been aroused. "All right, free him. And throw Harlequin on the fire instead. I must have my meat well roasted!" Just think of poor Harlequin! He had saved Pinocchio, only to die himself! His knees buckled under him, and his head flopped forward. Two of the soldier puppets seized his arms and dragged him towards the flames.

At this awful sight! Pinocchio threw himself down before the puppet-master. "Have pity, Sir Fire-Eater! Pardon brave Harlequin. He has done you no wrong!"

"Impossible! The fire is already low and I must have my meat well roasted."

"In that case," said Pinocchio, "I know my duty. It's not right that

Suddenly, silence fell. The puppet-master, a ferocious looking giant called Fire-Eater with a long beard as black as ink, had burst on to the stage. His eyes were like burning coals, and in his hand was a hideous whip made of snakes and foxes' tails.

"Why do you dare to come into my theatre?" he bellowed. And he siezed Pinocchio and threw him into a log basket in the kitchen. The play started again, and when it finished Fire-Eater called to Punch, "bring that puppet here and throw it on the fire! I must have a good blaze to get my meat well roasted for supper!"

Pinocchio was brought in, struggling for his life and calling for help. Then his brother Harlequin went down on one knee. "O Fire-Eater," he cried, "spare our little brother. He's much too young to die."

Harlequin should die for me. Puppets, bind me and throw *me* into the flames!"

At these words, all the puppets burst into tears. How noble Pinocchio was! And how dreadful that he should come to a bad end! Then, suddenly, the room echoed to a deafening noise. Fire-Eater had sneezed again, not once but three times! And when he finally stopped he lifted Pinocchio into his arms.

"You're a good boy! Harlequin shall be freed, and tonight, just this once, I will have to eat my mutton half cooked."

Sitting Pinocchio on his knee, he asked him where he had come from, and who his father was. And when he heard that Geppetto was just a poor wood-carver, he began sneezing all over again. "Here, take these five gold pieces and give them to your father. And tell him to keep a better eye on you in the future! Now get home before I change my mind."

Pinocchio left the hall with the cheers of the puppets ringing in his ears. He was as happy as could be — now he could buy another schoolbook *and* give Geppetto a brand new coat. He whistled cheerfully as he marched back along the road, and at every step he tossed a coin high into the air, catching it as it fell.

He could hardly wait to see Geppetto's face!

Little did he know what fate had in store for him, or how long a journey he had begun. For he had not gone far when he met two travellers — a Fox, who was lame in one foot, and a Cat, who was blind in both eyes. These unfortunate creatures were helping each other along, the Fox leaning on the Cat's shoulder and showing him the way.

"Good day," said the Fox, politely.

"Good day, Mr Fox," replied Pinocchio, spinning a coin casually in the air.

The gold coin flashed in the sunlight. The Fox's lame paw twitched a little, and the Cat's blind eyes opened wide like two green lamps — but only for a fraction of a second.

"I say!" said the Fox as they all walked along together. "What a lot of money you have. And what will you spend it on, if I may ask?"

"First I shall buy a new coat for my father, and then I shall buy a spelling book. I'm going to school, to learn to be good."

"Oh dear," said the Fox. "Look at me. Through my long years of study I have lost the use of my paw."

"And look at me," said the Cat. "Through my long years of study I have gone blind!"

At that very moment, a blackbird perched in the hedge called out a warning. "Pinocchio, don't listen to those bad men . . ." But before he could finish, the Cat sprang on the bird and gulped him down in a single mouthful, feathers and all.

"Nothing but trouble, blackbirds," sneered the Cat.

They were all halfway to Pinocchio's house when the Fox suddenly stopped. "How would you like to double your money?" he asked.

Naturally Pinocchio was very interested, especially when the Cat explained that doubling your money was child's play. If you knew how, you could easily turn five gold coins into 500, or even 5,000!

"All you have to do," the Cat continued, "is to bury your money in the Field of Miracles. You water it, salt it, leave it for two hours, and then what do you find? Your money has grown into a magnificent tree, laden with hundreds of bright new coins."

Instantly, Pinocchio forgot all about his father, the new coat and the schoolbook. All he could think of was the wonderful Field of Miracles. He just *had* to see it. And at the very next turning the Fox and the Cat led him away down a narrow winding lane and out into the country.

The Field of Miracles

With his two shady companions, the Fox and the Cat, Pinocchio was still trudging along when the sun went down.

"Look!" said the Fox suddenly. "There's the Red Crab Inn. We can have a bite to eat, then press on at midnight to arrive at the Field of Miracles by dawn tomorrow!"

But when they sat down at the table, none of them, it seemed, had any appetite. The Cat could only squeeze down thirty-five helpings of fish and four helpings of tripe, while the Fox struggled gamely with a few dozen partridges, six rabbits and a hare. Pinocchio ate nothing at all — could think only of the great day to come.

After their snack, the Fox ordered rooms for the three of them, and they all went off to sleep, leaving firm instructions to be woken at midnight. But when the inn-keeper shook Pinocchio awake, he had strange news.

"The Fox and the Cat have been called away early. They will meet you at the Field of Miracles at sunrise, if you make your own way there. Oh, and would you mind paying the bill for all three of you . . .?"

Pinocchio handed over one of his five precious gold coins and hurried on his way.

Dark clouds covered the stars, so he whistled to help keep up his spirits. Everything seemed very eerie. Then, as the road led through a dense wood, Pinocchio heard a rusle of leaves behind him! There in the gloom were two hooded figures — and they were chasing him!

The robbers were catching up fast, so Pinocchio popped the four gold coins into his mouth and scrambled up a tree. Surely he would be safe

there! But looking down, he saw the robbers set fire to the tree, and in no time at all flames were darting up towards him.

Pinocchio made a huge leap down on to the ground and raced away again. He sprang across a large ditch, and turned to see the robbers fall in! But they were out again in a trice, and following as fast as ever. Then, as Pinocchio felt he could run no further, he saw a little cottage and staggered towards it. Just before he reached the door, powerful hands seized him by the throat and a hollow voice demanded, "Your money — or your life!"

Pinocchio shook his head. "Come on now, no nonsense! Where's that money? Tell us or we'll kill you!"

"No, no!" cried poor Pinocchio — and the coins clinked in his mouth.

"So, you cheat! The money is under your tongue. Well, we know how to shake it out of there!" And with a horrible noise, like a Fox snarling, the taller of the two robbers pulled a noose from under his cloak and slipped it over Pinocchio's head. Seconds later, the poor puppet was dangling from the nearest tree.

The two robbers slunk away. "We'll be back tomorrow, when you'll be dead, with your mouth hanging open."

As Pinocchio's flimsy body swung in the night wind, he thought of all the warnings he had been given, until his breath failed him and he hung stiff and silent.

Now, the owner of the cottage was a beautiful Fairy, who had lived in the wood for more than a thousand years. And she had seen everything from her window. As soon as the robbers were out of sight the Fairy sent her very best carriage, driven by a poodle and drawn by a hundred pairs of white mice, to bring the limp body of Pinocchio to the cottage.

Soon, at his bedside, stood three worried doctors — and owl, a crow and a cricket — discussing their patient. And what should Pinocchio hear first as he woke, but the voice of the cricket. "I've seen that puppet before. He's a good-for-nothing rogue, a disobedient son who will make his poor father die of a broken heart."

Pinocchio burst into tears, But the sound of his sobs made the doctors happy, for their patient was obviously alive. "When a *dead* person cries, it is a sign that he is getting much better," droned the owl. "I think we may leave now, gentlemen." And out of the door they went.

Then the Fairy felt Pinocchio's forehead. He still had a high temperature and was very ill, so she made him some medicine. But because it was bitter, the puppet refused to take it. And when the Fairy gave him sugar to sweeten the taste, he crunched down the sugar and refused the medicine!

At that the door swung open and four black rabbits entered the room, carrying a coffin for Pinocchio.

"We have come to take you away," said the head rabbit.

"To take me?" squealed Pinocchio. "But I'm not dead! Fairy, oh Fairy, give me the medicine, please!" And Pinocchio downed the bitter liquid in one swallow.

"What a waste of out time," grumbled the rabbits. "That's another journey made for nothing." And they all trooped out of the room muttering.

A few minutes later, Pinocchio was well again. This is quite normal, you know. Wooden puppets are not often ill for long!

He told the Fairy the whole story and boasted about how clever he had been to hide the gold under his tongue.

"But where's the gold now?" asked the Fairy.

"Um, I've lost it!" said Pinocchio — and at once his nose began to grow!

"And where exactly did you lose it?"

"Um, in the wood." And his nose grew even more. "No, I remember. I didn't lose it. I swallowed it." And with that enormous fib his nose grew so long that he could not turn around. If he turned left, his nose struck the bed. And if he turned right it hit the window-pane!

"You're lying, Pinocchio," smiled the Fairy. And she explained to him that every time he told a lie his nose would grow. Poor Pinocchio was in misery, and the Fairy had to stifle her laughter. So she called a flock of woodpeckers to trim his enormous nose back to its usual size.

"How kind you are, Fairy," he said humbly. "I love you so much."

"I love you to, Pinocchio, and I will always look after you. But now you must forget all about the Field of Miracles and go home to your father, Geppetto. He is worried to death about you."

So Pinocchio kissed the Fairy goodbye and hurried off through the wood. But just as he was passing the tree where the robbers had strung him up, who should he meet but the Fox and Cat.

"Why, here is our dear Pinocchio," cried the Fox, hugging him tight. "What are you doing here?"

"Yes, what are you doing here?" asked the Cat.

Pinocchio told his story once again, while the two crafty animals pretended to be amazed. How sad they were to hear his tale! And how helpful they would be!

You can guess what happened. In no time at all Pinocchio had forgotten Geppetto and set off for the Field of Miracles with the Fox and the Cat.

After a long march, which took them half a day, they came to a town called Trap o' Fools, where the streets were crowded with hundreds of poor beggars. And a mile further on they reached an empty field — a field that looked exactly like every other field they had passed.

"Here we are at last," puffed the Fox. "Now kneel down and dig a little hole. That's it, now put the coins in. Sprinkle this pinch of salt over them, and fill the hole again."

"Is that all I have to do?"

"Well, just pour on a little water. Good, that's perfect. We'll all go away now, but if you come back in two hours' time you'll find a thick bush poking through the ground, with its branches weighed down with gold!"

Pinocchio could not thank his friends enough. He wanted them to stay, and take at least a thousand of the new coins as a reward for their help. But the Cat would not hear of it. "We need no reward. It's quite enough for us to see you so wealthy and contended." So saying, they all shook hands and parted on the very best of terms.

Pinocchio walked back to Trap o'

Fools and counted the minutes on the church clock. When the two hours were nearly up he hurried off to collect his gold. His head was full of plans about how he would spend the money and help Geppetto. But when he entered the field again, he could see nothing. Absolutely nothing.

With an awful sinking feeling in his stomach, Pinocchio ran to the place where he had buried the coins. The hole had been dug open again, and was completely empty! As Pinocchio fell to his knees in despair he heard a low cackle of laughter from the tree behind him. Looking round he saw a large parrot, preening its feathers.

"Ah, what a fool you are, I nearly died laughing when I saw you plant that gold. That crafty old Fox and Cat came back while you were away, dug up the coins and fled like the wind!"

With the shrieks of the parrot ringing in his ears, Pinocchio hurried back to Trap o' Fools and went straight to the Law Court to demand justice. He was called before the chief judge, a wise old gorilla, and accused the Cat and the Fox of fraud and robbery. When the judge had heard the evidence, he rapped his mallet on the table and passed judgement.

"You are a fool, Pinocchio, and fools must be trapped. Since you have lost *four* gold coins, you will go straight to jail and stay there *four* months." And with a hollow clang, the prison doors slammed shut on poor Pinocchio, the puppet who just could not be good.

The Great Search

After four long months in prison, Pinocchio was finally set free. And when the iron doors swung open his only thought was to hurry away from the horrible Trap o' Fools. First he would visit the Fairy, and then he would go home to his father, Geppetto.

The road was muddy from days of rain but Pinocchio skipped along merrily until, turning a corner, he found his way completely blocked. An enormous snake with glaring red eyes, and smoke billowing from its tail lay right across the path!

Pinocchio was too scared to try and pass the snake, so he waited at a safe distance for it to move. But the snake just stayed where it was, staring at him with its fiery eyes. At last, Pinocchio summoned up all his courage, walked right up to the snake, and asked very politely if it would let him pass. To his amazement, the snake immediately lay down and closed its eyes — even its tail stopped smoking. "He must be dead," thought Pinocchio, and he tried to jump over the body. But just as he took off, the snake reared up angrily and Pinocchio was thrown backwards and landed head down in the mud!

The snake had only been playing, and now it burst into a great fit of giggles at the sight of the puppet's wriggling, upside-down body. But it laughed so much at its own joke that it suddenly split its sides . . . and collapsed!

This time the snake really *was* dead, so Pinocchio picked himself up, clambered over it, and ran on down the path. After all the excitement he felt very hungry, so when he saw some juicy grapes growing in a field, he climbed over the fence to pick a bunch. It was a big mistake, for just as he was stretching out his hand there was a loud crack — as the jaws of a hideous iron trap snapped fast around his legs.

Poor Pinocchio screamed and yelled for hours, but no-one came. Then, through the gloom, a farmer appeared.

"Well, well, what have we got here? Ha! So it's you that's been catching my chickens! And I thought it was weasels!"

"It wasn't me, really it wasn't! I only wanted some grapes!"

"Anyone who steals grapes is quite capable of stealing chickens. You're coming with me to the farmyard. My guard-dog died this morning, so you can take his place!"

And, to Pinocchio's horror, the farmer buckled a heavy dog collar around his neck and chained him to a kennel!

"If you see any of those thieving weasels you bark at once! Understand?" Then the farmer went off to bed, leaving the puppet with a bowl of water and an old bone.

Pinocchio lay down on the straw. Oh, how miserable he was! Finally he cried himself to sleep, but soon he was woken by strange noises. There, right inside the farmyard, were four large weasels. One of them tip-toed over to the kennel.

"Evening, Melampo."

"I'm not Melampo. He's dead. I'm a puppet, and I'm here as a punishment."

"Never mind, never mind. We'll give you the same deal as we had with Melampo. If you keep quiet, and let us take eight chickens each week, there'll be one plump chicken for you. All right?"

"Well, I'm . . ." and before Pinocchio could say more, the weasels had opened the door to the chicken-house nearby and slipped inside.

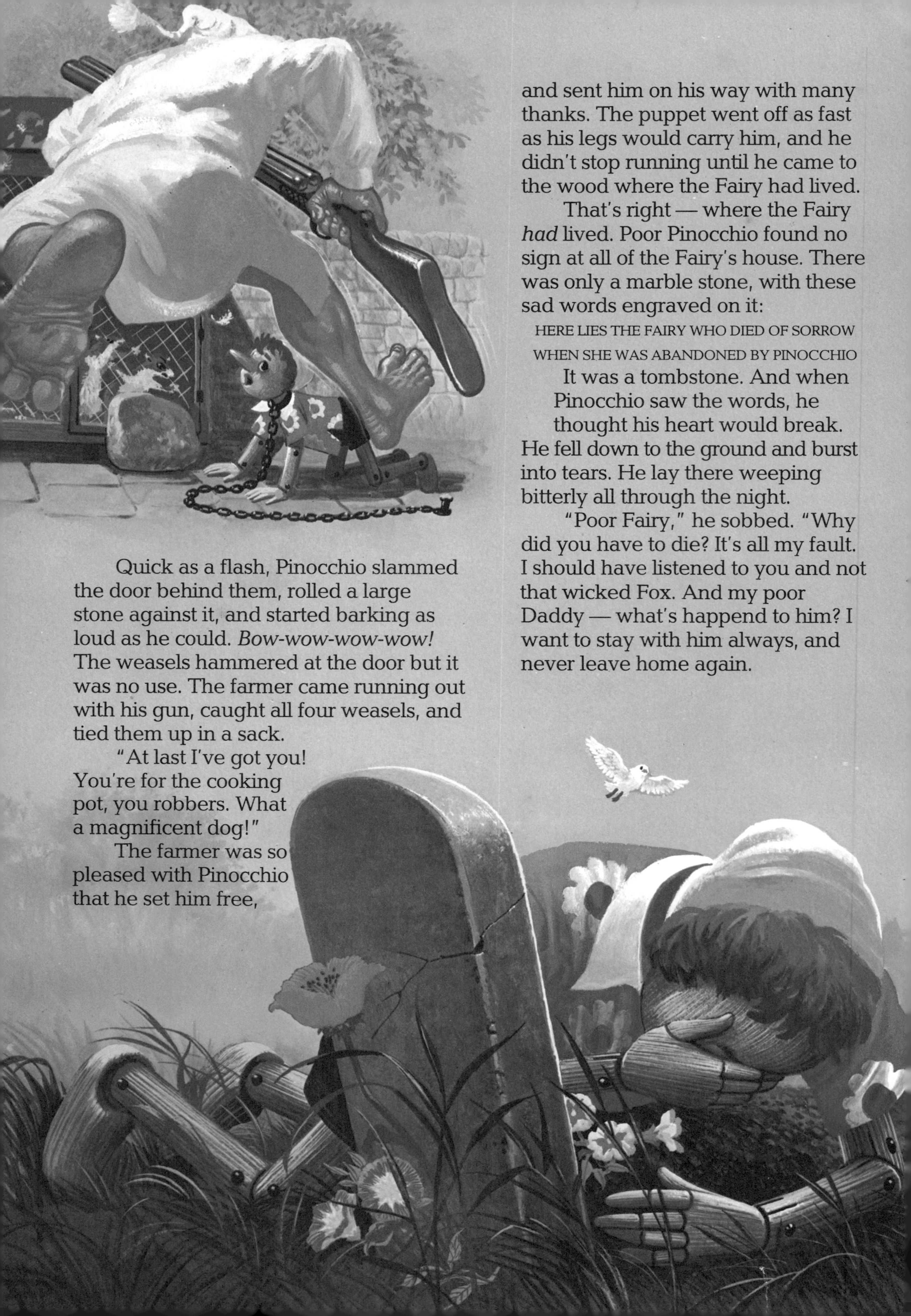

Quick as a flash, Pinocchio slammed the door behind them, rolled a large stone against it, and started barking as loud as he could. *Bow-wow-wow-wow!* The weasels hammered at the door but it was no use. The farmer came running out with his gun, caught all four weasels, and tied them up in a sack.

"At last I've got you! You're for the cooking pot, you robbers. What a magnificent dog!"

The farmer was so pleased with Pinocchio that he set him free, and sent him on his way with many thanks. The puppet went off as fast as his legs would carry him, and he didn't stop running until he came to the wood where the Fairy had lived.

That's right — where the Fairy *had* lived. Poor Pinocchio found no sign at all of the Fairy's house. There was only a marble stone, with these sad words engraved on it:

HERE LIES THE FAIRY WHO DIED OF SORROW
WHEN SHE WAS ABANDONED BY PINOCCHIO

It was a tombstone. And when Pinocchio saw the words, he thought his heart would break. He fell down to the ground and burst into tears. He lay there weeping bitterly all through the night.

"Poor Fairy," he sobbed. "Why did you have to die? It's all my fault. I should have listened to you and not that wicked Fox. And my poor Daddy — what's happend to him? I want to stay with him always, and never leave home again.

Oh Fairy, please come back to life. Don't leave me here alone."

And Pinocchio wished that he could die himself.

Then, in the green light of dawn, a huge dove flew overhead. Hovering above the tombstone, it called down to the puppet, "Is that you, Pinocchio? I have been looking for you everywhere." And when Pinocchio nodded sadly, the great bird landed behind him, breathless with news.

"You must come quickly! Your father Geppetto is about to sail away. You have been lost so long he thought you must have gone to another land. He has built himself a boat, to cross the ocean and search for you."

Pinocchio sprang on to the dove's back and away they flew, soaring high above the clouds. He was so scared of falling that he hung on tightly with both hands. There was a long, long way to go, so they flew all day, and they flew all night. And early the next morning the dove left Pinocchio on a stony beach.

A crowd of people were there, shouting and waving out to sea. "What's happened?" cried Pinocchio. "Tell me, please." An old woman explained. "A father has set out in a tiny boat to find his lost son. But now the storm has blown up and he is sure to drown!"

Pinocchio scrambled up a high rock and stared out to sea. Sure enough, there in the distance, was Geppetto, waving helplessly back to shore. "Daddy, I'm coming!" shouted Pinocchio. "I'll save you!" But at that very moment a huge wave crashed down on the boat, and it was seen no more.

Pinocchio dived into the foaming waters and swam through the storm. He floated easily because he was made of wood, but the wind soon blew him off course. The rain lashed the sea in torrents, thunder crashed and lightning split the sky. Hour after hour the puppet was hurled about like a bundle of sticks — and then one enormous wave lifted him clear out of the water and dumped him down on a sandy shore.

Pinocchio lay exhausted on the beach as, little by little, the sky cleared and the sea became calm. He laid his clothes out to dry in the sun, and sat gazing across the water for Geppetto's little boat. Wherever he looked he could see nothing. But then a large fish came swimming round the bay, close to the shore.

"Excuse me, Mr Fish," called Pinocchio.

"Yes, young man," replied the fish, who was in fact a Dolphin, and very friendly.

"Have you see a little boat with my Daddy in it?"

"Oh dear," said the Dolphin, "was that your father? During the storm he and his boat were swallowed by a shark. You poor boy — you won't see him again, I'm afraid!" And he swam sadly away.

Poor Pinocchio. First he loses the Fairy, and now his father, Geppetto. He put his clothes on, and with his heart as heavy as lead followed the road away from the beach. After an hour he came to a place called Busy Bee Village, where the streets were full of people all working at their trades. Wherever he looked there was not a single person idle.

"This won't suit me," thought Pinocchio. "I hate working."

By now he was very thirsty, so he asked a young woman, who was carrying two pails of water, if he could have a drink.

"Of course you can. Here, drink up." And Pinocchio guzzled as if he had never drunk water before.

"And I'll give you some bread and stew if you'll help me with these pails."

"But I hate working. I'm not a donkey, you know!"

"*And* some syrup pudding!"

Pinocchio was so ravenous he could not resist. "All right then. I'll carry this smaller one to your house."

They struggled up the road with the heavy pails, and as soon as they were inside her house the woman gave Pinocchio his bread and stew and syrup pudding. He gobbled them down as if he had never eaten before.

When he had finished he looked up at the young woman — and there before him was the very face, with the same hair and the same eyes, that he had thought never to see again.

"O Fairy, it's *you*! You're *alive*! I thought I'd lost you for ever, like Daddy. I've been so unhappy — *please* don't make me cry again."

And he threw himself down on the floor and hugged her knees.

The Fairy smiled and stroked his head, then she picked him up and kissed him.

"I'm glad to see you too, Pinocchio. Will you stay with me now, like a good boy?" "Yes, I promise!"

The Fairy's Promise

Pinocchio had settled down happily at the Fairy's house on Busy Bee Island. But something was bothering him. "I'm fed up with being a puppet," he suddenly said one day. "I want to become a *real* boy, and grow up to be a man!"

"Oh, that won't be so easy," replied the Fairy. "Puppets never grow. But if you are very good perhaps we can make an exception — if you deserve it. No more lies, mind, and no more lazing about round here! You'll have to go to school, and work hard!"

"You mean I *can* become a *real* boy?" shouted Pinocchio, dancing with glee.

"If you work hard for a whole year and stop all your naughty habits, I promise that you will become a real boy. So off you go to school, tomorrow!"

You can imagine what it was like when he first arrived.

The other boys thought it was hilarious to have a puppet in their class, and they played all kinds of nasty tricks on him. But when they pulled Pinocchio's long nose, he set about them with his wooden feet and wooden fists until they learned to show some respect.

Within a few weeks he was friends with almost everyone. But there was one thing the others still held against him — he was already top of the class.

So one fine day, some of them stopped Pinocchio on his way to school and told him that a huge whale had been seen near the coast. "We're going to sneak off school and see for ourselves. Why don't you come along too?"

Pinocchio wanted to wait until after school, but the boys all laughed at him. "The whale won't wait all day for you!"

So, once again, poor Pinocchio was led astray. But it was not long before he realised he had been completely fooled. There was no whale to be seen, and the sea was as smooth as a mirror.

"He must have gone off for his breakfast!" jeered one of the boys. "Or perhaps he's having a nap! laughed another.

Pinocchio was furious. And the more the boys laughed at him, the angrier he got. Before you knew it, a great fight had broken out and schoolbooks and satchels were being thrown in all directions.

In all the confusion, one of the boys was struck on the forehead by a flying book and sank to the ground, as white as a sheet. At this dreadful sight, the other boys ran off as fast as they could, leaving Pinocchio alone with their fallen friend.

The puppet was still there, bathing the boy's head with a handkerchief soaked in sea-water, when two policemen appeared behind him with a dog.

"You'd better come along with us. This boy is badly hurt. You're under arrest." And summoning an old man from a nearby cottage to care for the injured boy, they dragged Pinocchio back along the road towards town.

The little puppet was absolutely terrified. His legs trembled and his tongue stuck to the roof of his mouth so that he could not speak — even to tell them *he* had not thrown the book. But just as he thought he would die of fright, a gust of wind blew his cap back towards the beach. The policemen let him run after it, and Pinocchio seized his chance to escape!

This only made matters worse. The policemen unleashed their prize bulldog — a huge savage beast called Alidoro. Soon Pinocchio could hear it panting close behind him. Then he could feel the dog's hot breath on the back of his legs. Now he was almost at the cliff edge . . . and with a last desperate leap, he flung himself into the waves and swam out.

Alidoro tried hard to stop, digging his paws into the ground, but his speed carried him deep into the water. The poor dog could not swim! He struggled to keep afloat, but it was no good. As he came to the surface for the third time, his eyes were rolling with terror and he barked piteously. "Help me, Pinocchio! Save me from drowning!"

When he heard this feeble cry, Pinocchio's heart melted. He swam quickly back to drag the dog ashore, then dived into the waves once more and swam off. The grateful words of the bulldog followed him, "Goodbye, Pinocchio! You saved my life!"

The puppet swam on round the coast, looking for a safe place to come ashore.

At last, reaching a rocky headland, Pinocchio saw a plume of smoke rising from a dark cave. He swam close to take a better look, and was just about to climb ashore when suddenly he felt himself being hoisted clean out of the water. He had been caught in a fishing net and was trapped in a shoal of wriggling fish! At that very moment, a gigantic fisherman emerged from the cave.

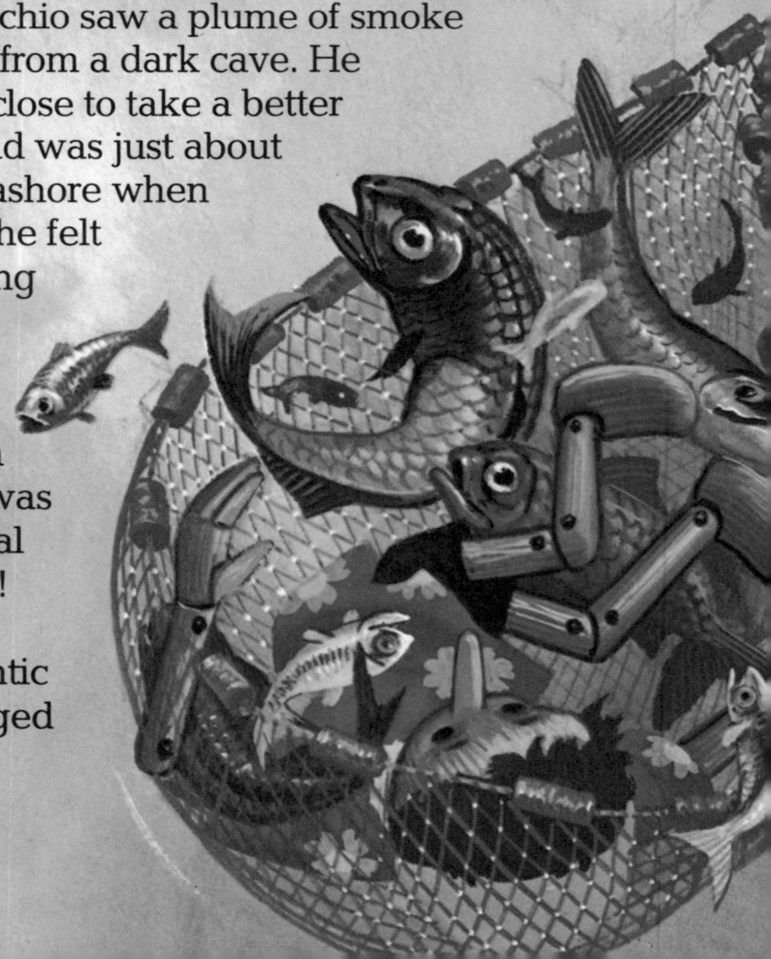

He was as ugly as a sea monster, and scaly all over. His head was covered with a thatch of seaweed, his scaly body was green, his bulging eyes were green and his beard was long and slimy.

"So, another good catch today," he growled, hauling in the net. And he stamped back into the cave, where a huge frying pan was sizzling over the log fire.

"Now then, what have we got here? This mullet looks good." And one by one he seized the fish, dabbed them in the flour, and tossed them into the pan. "Oh, these sardines look delicious! And what beautiful whiting! But what's this? This is a new one!"

And he plucked poor Pinocchio out of the net, all dripping wet and shaking with fear.

"I'm not a fish, I'm a puppet! Please let me go! I won't taste very nice!"

"Let you go? You must be joking! Do you think I'd miss the chance of tasting such a rare fish? I've never caught a puppet before!" He rolled Pinocchio slowly in the flour — well seasoned with salt and pepper — and held him over the pan.

Just then there was a great growl and in rushed Alidoro, drawn to the cave by the wonderful smell of cooking.

"Get out!" shouted the fisherman, trying to kick the dog.

"Save me, Alidoro!" cried Pinocchio, struggling pathetically in the giant's hand.

The faithful hound leaped into the air, snatched the floury puppet from the giant's grasp and bolted out of the cave.

Alidoro carried Pinocchio back to the beach where their adventure had started. "There!" he said. "You save me first — now I've saved you. In this world we must all help each other." And Alidoro licked the puppet warmly before heading off again in search of his masters.

It was late in the day now, and Pinocchio was eager to get home. The road to the village took him past an old man's cottage, where he was told that the injured boy had recovered and that the police were no longer searching for him. It was a great relief, but the puppet was still worried about owning up to the Fairy.

"What on earth will she say?" he fretted. "I'm sure she will never forgive me. And it serves me right. I always promise to be good, but I never keep my word.

I'll never become a *real* boy!"

By the time Pinocchio reached the Fairy's house, night had fallen and he was cold and tired and very hungry. But when he knocked on the door, there was silence. Had the Fairy left him again? He waited and waited. At last, after half an hour, a window opened at the top of the house, and a big snail looked out, with a lighted lamp balanced on her head.

"Who's there at this time of night?" she asked.

"It's me, Pinocchio. Is the Fairy home?"

"The Fairy is asleep and must not be woken. But I will come down and let you in."

An hour passed, and then two, but still the door did not open. Pinocchio was freezing cold, so he knocked again. This time a window on the third floor opened. The snail looked out again. "My dear boy, there's no use knocking like that. I'm a snail — and snails never hurry." And she pulled the window shut.

Shortly afterwards, midnight struck, then one o'clock, and then two — and the door was still closed.

Poor Pinocchio! There was nothing he could do but wait. He stood there by the door all night, until at dawn the door finally opened. The snail had taken nine hours to come all the way downstairs!

"You cannot come in yet," she said. "The Fairy is still asleep."

"Then at least bring me something to

eat!" pleaded the puppet, "I'm starving!"

"At once," said the snail — and she returned two hours later with bread, roast chicken and fruit, all on a silver tray. Pinocchio tore hungrily at the food, but to his horror he found that none of it was real. It was all made of cardboard! Exhausted by all his dreadful ordeals, he fainted.

When he came to, he was lying on a sofa inside the house, with the Fairy beside him. She was not angry, but she gave Pinocchio a solemn warning: "You know you've done wrong. I will pardon you once more. But woe betide you if you behave badly a third time . . ."

Pinocchio promised again and again to change his ways for ever. And this time he meant it. He never wanted to go through a day and night like that again!

He had learned his lesson, and he kept his word perfectly for one whole year. The following summer he won the prize for the best student at the school, and his behaviour was so good that the Fairy was delighted. When he came home from school she said, "Your wish shall be granted. You shall be a wooden puppet no longer. Tomorrow night you will become a *real* boy!"

In bed that night, Pinocchio could hardly sleep he was so excited. Only one more day! If only he could be good for just one more day!

Journey into Playland

"Just think, Pinocchio," said the Fairy. "At midnight you'll become a *real boy*! We must have a party to celebrate. Run out now and invite all your friends to come round. But don't be long. Make sure you're back before dark."

"I'll be back. I promise!" shouted the happy puppet, and he raced out of the house, jumping and dancing as he went.

Pinocchio ran from door to door, spreading his good news. Everyone promised to come to the party. But his very best friend — a lazy scamp they all called Candlewick because he was so thin — was nowhere to be found.

Pinocchio kept on searching. He ran right through all the streets three times — and eventually found his friend sitting just outside the village.

"What are you doing here?" asked Pinocchio.

"I'm waiting for the magic coach, which comes past here at nightfall. And then I'm going far, far away."

"But I've come to invite you to my party. Haven't you heard? At midnight I shall become a *real boy*!"

"Much good that will do you," sneered Candlewick. "Look, forget your silly party and come with me to Playland. It's the best place in the world. There are no schools and no teachers, and all you do is play from morning to night!"

"No, no, I can't. I'm late already, and I promised the Fairy I would be home before dark."

"Don't worry about her. All she ever does is scold you, anyway." And Candlewick told Pinocchio all about the fabulous land where summer holidays last all year.

But twilight was falling now, and Pinocchio turned to walk home. Then, suddenly, in the distance, there was the sound of a bugle. The coach was coming! Lights twinkled in the darkness, and there it was — pulled by four donkeys, all wearing white leather boots!

Dozens of boys were packed inside, all chatting excitedly. The jolly coachman — a little round man with a face like a tomato and a laughing mouth — hauled

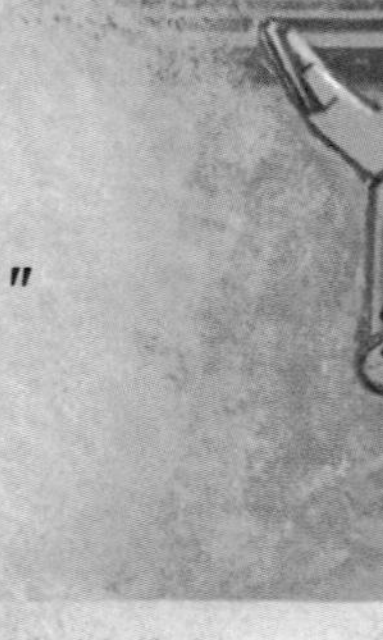

Candlewick on board, then turned to Pinocchio. "And what about you, my lad? Are you coming with us, or are you staying behind?

"I must go home, sir. I'm already late, and the Fairy will be cross with me."

No, no! Come with us to Playland!" called the boys from the coach. "Remember, no more school! No more teachers! Fun and games from morning to night!"

Pinocchio just could not resist. He gave a deep sigh, then said quietly, "All right, *I'll come*!"

The coach was so crowded that there was no room inside, so Pinocchio tried to climb on to a donkey. At once the animal reared up and kicked him into the road! All the boys giggled as Pinocchio angrily climbed up again from the other side. And again the donkey kicked him off! The coachman was furious. He jumped down into the road and gave it a hearty whack with his stick. Then he lifted Pinocchio on to the animal's back.

All through the long night's journey the poor donkey was in tears, and it kept whispering to Pinocchio, in a voice rather like a small boy's: "You stupid puppet! One day you'll be crying too. You never listen to good advice. You'll come to a bad end, like me. Just you wait and see!"

The coach rattled along hour after hour until, just after sunrise, it rolled into Playland. what a fabulous sight it was! There were boys playing everywhere you looked — running and jumping, shouting and laughing, playing with toys and balls and skates and bicycles. Some were dressed as soldiers, others made up like clowns. There were playgrounds and carousels, sandpits and theatres. The whole place was such a riot of fun that the new boys jumped straight down from the coach and plunged into the thick of it! How happy they all were!

The weeks passed like lightning. Pinocchio spent every minute playing, and never once regretted leaving home. "What a wonderful life!" said the puppet each time he met his friend. "And to think you wanted to go back to the Fairy," laughed Candlewick. "You're lucky to have me for a friend."

Then, one morning, after months of bliss, Pinocchio woke up to the most unpleasant shock he had ever had. His ears were long and brown and hairy — just like a donkey's!

The poor puppet was so ashamed that he burst into tears, and beat his head against the wall.

But the more he cried, the longer his ears grew! Finally, in despair, he pulled a long cotton cap right over his head to hide his ears and rushed off to find Candlewick.

At first his friend would not let him in and Pinocchio had to wait outside. But after half an hour the door slowly opened. And there stood Candlewick with a cap just like Pinocchio's, pulled right down over *his* long, hairy ears! You can imagine how foolish the two boys felt. For a few moments they stood in the middle of the room in silence. But then, instead of crying or consoling each other, they burst out laughing! At the count of three, they tore off their caps and threw them into the air and they started capering around the room, giggling and waggling their long hairy ears.

They laughed and laughed, until suddenly Candlewick stopped laughing and fell to his knees. Pinocchio looked down at him in amazement, then collapsed himself. Kneeling on the ground, they watched in horror as their hands turned into hooves, their faces lengthened into muzzles, and their backs sprouted coats of thick hair. And, worst of all, they each grew a long tail!

Then came a loud knock at the door. "Open up at once! You donkeys belong to me!" And the coachman just kicked open the door and marched in.

He put bridles around their necks and led them off to the market place. Candlewick was bought by a farmer, who sent him to work in the fields. And Pinocchio was sold to a circus. The circus ringmaster was not a cruel man, but he would not stand for any nonsense. When his new donkey refused to eat hay, he struck him with a whip. And then he drove Pinocchio into the circus ring and taught him to jump through hoops, to dance waltzes and polkas, and to stand upright on his hind legs.

After three months of hard training — with a sound thrashing whenever he jumped badly — Pinocchio gave his first public performance. People came from miles around to see the amazing donkey, and the circus was packed an hour before the start.

The ringmaster cracked his whip, and in ran Pinocchio, the star attraction. He went round and round the ring, trotting, cantering, galloping. As the crowd cheered wildly at his wonderful performance, Pinocchio raised his head in pride and looked round the audience. And who should he see but the Fairy!

Pinocchio dashed across the ring and tried to call to her, but being a donkey all he did was bray. The audience howled with laughter . . . but the ringmaster was furious, and gave him a crack on the nose with his whip. The blow brought tears to Pinocchio's eyes, and by the time he could see again, the Fairy seemed to have gone! Imagine how desperate poor Pinocchio felt! He tried twice to dive through the hoop, but failed both times. And at the third attempt, he fell so badly that he hurt his leg.

It was a disaster for the circus. The very next day, the ringmaster sent him straight back to the market, where a drum-maker who wanted a donkey skin to make a drum bought poor, hungry Pinocchio for just ten pence. Then the man led the crippled donkey down to the sea-shore. Tying a rope to his muzzle, he pushed him into the water to drown!

After half an hour the drum-maker hauled in the rope, thinking the donkey must be quite dead by now. But when he gave one final tug, instead of a dead donkey, he pulled out Pinocchio struggling and wriggling like an eel!

The poor man could not believe his eyes. He had thrown in a donkey — and pulled out a puppet.

"Where's my donkey?" he yelled.

"I'm your donkey!" laughed Pinocchio. "The fishes nibbled away at the carcass — and left only me! They must have been summoned by the Fairy!"

And with a cheeky wave, he slipped the rope from his nose and dived into the sea.

He was free again, and safe. Now if only he could find the dear Fairy . . .

Home and Dry

Pinocchio was in such a hurry to escape from Playland and the drum-maker that he swam far out to sea, until all that could be seen of him was a tiny black speck on the horizon. He was so happy to be free that every now and then he swung his legs out of the water and waggled them above the surface, like a dolphin's tail.

He swam for hours, not really caring which way he went. Then, suddenly, he glimpsed a strange sight. Towering out of the waves was a rock of pure white marble, and on the top stood a beautiful little goat, which was bleating to him in a very friendly way, and nodding excitedly.

Most surprising of all, the goat's hair was blue! And Pinocchio realised that it was not a normal goat at all, but his Good Fairy in disguise, come to rescue him again.

His heart began beating at twice its usual rate, and he swam towards the goat with all his strength. But before he was halfway to the marble rock, a huge monster shark reared up and out of the water! Pinocchio felt himself drawn helplessly towards its massive mouth, and its three rows of enormous jagged teeth!

Just think of Pinocchio's terror! He struggled to change direction. He cried piteously for help. And the blue goat called out in anguish, "Swim quickly Pinocchio! The shark will get you!"

But it was already too late! Gigantic jaws closed around the wriggling puppet, and everything went dark. Pinocchio felt himself sliding down the monster's throat, and into its vast stomach — and then he blacked out.

When Pinocchio came to, he was terribly scared. It was very dark, and eerily silent. From time to time there was a strange rasping noise, and great gusts of wind blew into his face. It was the shark breathing! Poor Pinocchio felt so lost and alone that he cried and screamed. "Help, help! Save me! Won't someone save me?"

Then, out of the gloom, came a low voice. "No-one will save you, unhappy wretch. You can do nothing but wait to be digested!"

"Who's that?" stammered Pinocchio, shaking with fear.

"It is I, a poor Tuna fish, who was swallowed by the shark just before you. But I do not cry or yell. I am a philosopher. I count myself lucky to be eaten by a fish, and not by humans!"

"But I don't want to be eaten at *all!*" cried the puppet. "I want to escape! How big is this shark, and where's the way out?"

"There is no way out," replied the Tuna, with a voice of doom. "The shark is a mile long — and that's not counting his tail!"

Left alone with the Tuna, Pinocchio might have given up hope, but while they were talking he saw a tiny light twinkling in the distance. So, saying goodbye, he groped his way along the body of the shark. It took a long time for him to reach the flickering light, but when he finally arrived, he could hardly believe his eyes.

He found a little old man, with a long white beard, sitting at a table with a lighted candle stuck into a bottle!

And who do you think the old man was? Yes, it was Geppetto, the wood-carver — Pinocchio's own dear father! The puppet was overcome with joy.

"Oh Daddy, Daddy, I've found you at last, after all this time."

And he did not know whether to laugh or cry at the old man's astonished face.

"Do my old eyes deceive me? Is it really you, Pinocchio? I thought I had lost you forever." And he hugged his son as if he would never let go. "I have been in this shark for two years, since that fateful day when I set sail in my little boat. I saw the white dove leave you on the beach, and tried hard to return to shore. But the waves blew up and hurled me to the shark!"

"But how have you survived, Daddy?"

"In that same dreadful storm, a merchant ship was wrecked and the shark swallowed all its cargo. For these two years I have lived off the ship's supplies — corned beef, biscuits, cheese and sugar. There were even bottles of wine. But now I have nothing left and this is the very last candle!"

Hearing this, Pinocchio was more determined than ever to escape. Taking the candle in one hand, he led his poor father off into the darkness. For more than an hour they struggled along the belly of the shark, until they arrived at the back of the monster's mouth.

Peering through, beyond the jagged teeth, they could see the bright moon and a starry sky.

The shark was fast asleep, with his mouth wide open.

"Quick, Daddy, we must get out before the monster wakes!"

And, as the shark's snoring thundered in their ears, they climbed silently along its tongue, across its rows of teeth, and out on to its giant lip.

Then Pinocchio took Geppetto on his shoulders, leaped into the water, and swam away. The sea was calm and silent . . . and the shark was still sleeping like a log!

Pinocchio swam for hours, carrying his poor father — who could not swim a stroke. When dawn broke, the puppet was getting very tired and there was still no sign of land. Then, just as he felt he could move his arms and legs no more, he heard a familiar voice. "No need to panic. I will have you on dry land in a few minutes."

It was the Tuna. And as Pinocchio and Geppetto clambered thankfully on to his back, he explained how he had followed their example and escaped from the snoring shark.

The awful dangers were finally over. The Tuna left them safely on a sandy beach and Pinocchio thanked him again and again. Then the puppet and his father walked slowly inland, looking for food and shelter.

They had not gone far when they met two creatures begging by the roadside. They were the Fox and the Cat, who had fallen on hard times.

The Fox really *had* gone lame, and the Cat really *had* gone blind.

"Dear Pinocchio," whined the Fox. "Give a little charity to the needy!"

"Yes, my dear boy," pleaded the Cat. "Do help the aged and infirm!"

But Pinocchio and Geppetto ignored the wicked pair. "If you are poor now, you deserve it. You won't catch me out again!"

On they went, and a little further down the road they saw a pretty little cottage in the middle of a field. They walked across to knock at the door.

"Turn the key and the door will open," came a voice from inside.

So in they went — and there, high up on a beam, was the Talking Cricket! "Oh my dear little Cricket, how nice to see you," said Pinocchio, bowing politely.

"So! *Dear little Cricket*, is it? You didn't say that when you threw a mallet at me! You had no pity for me, but I will have pity on you. Just you remember from now on — it pays to be kind to people when you can!"

And the Cricket told Pinocchio that he had been given the cottage the day before by a beautiful blue-haired goat, who had gone away bleating in sorrow about a puppet that had been swallowed by a shark.

Deeply moved, and determined to be good, the puppet helped his tired father to lie down on a bed of straw, then went off in search of milk for him to drink. A nearby farmer offered him a jug, but only at a price.

Pinocchio had to do hours of back-breaking labour, drawing a hundred buckets of water from the well, to pay for the milk.

"Up till now I had a donkey to do this work," said the farmer. "I bought him a few months ago, at the market. But he was a lazy devil, always trying to dodge off. Then he fell sick, and how he's dying over there in the stable."

When Pinocchio ran over to look, he was amazed. For there, lying stretched out on the straw, was his old friend Candlewick. The poor sick donkey opened his eyes for the last time, gave a deep, groaning sigh . . . and died.

From then on, for many months Pinocchio worked for the farmer every day from dawn to dusk, to buy milk for his father and earn a few extra pennies for their daily needs. He learned to weave baskets from reeds and, whenever he could, he practised reading and writing. He worked so hard that after six months he had managed to save up fifty pence. So the next morning he set off for the market to buy himself a new shirt.

It was a beautiful day. The sun was shining and the birds were singing in the trees. The puppet was scampering along merrily, when all at once he saw a big snail, who called out to him, "Pinocchio! Stop!"

It was the Fairy's Snail, who had taken so long to let the puppet into her house the evening after he had been caught by the giant green fisherman!

"My beautiful Snail! What are you doing here? Do you know where the Fairy is?"

"Oh Pinocchio, the poor Fairy is very ill in hospital, and is likely to die! She has no money left to buy herself food."

At once the puppet snatched the fifty pence from his pocket and gave the coins to the Snail. "Quickly, take this money to the Fairy! I don't need a new shirt — these rags are enough for me." Without another word, the Snail raced off at high speed — quite unlike her normal self.

Pinocchio went straight back to the cottage and started work. Now he had *two* people to support — Geppetto *and* the Fairy. He slaved away making baskets until midnight, then curled up on his bed of straw and fell sound asleep.

And, as he slept, he dreamed he saw the Fairy. She was more beautiful than ever. She smiled at him, and kissed him gently. Then she said softly, "You're a good boy, Pinocchio. You have worked hard for Geppetto and for me in our time of need. I forgive you all your naughty past. And I promise you that if you are good in the future, you will always be happy."

With these words, the dream ended and Pinocchio woke up with a start. Everything was different! Pinocchio suddenly realised that he was no longer a puppet! He had become a *real* boy, just like other boys! The little cottage had become his old home, and his rags had turned into new clothes!

Just imagine how happy Pinocchio felt! The Fairy had kept her promise! At last, Pinocchio was a *real* boy! Pulling on his smart new trousers, he found a leather purse in the pocket. A note from the Fairy read: *Thank you Pinocchio, for the loan of fifty pence.* And inside the purse were fifty bright new shining coins!

Bursting with joy, Pinocchio ran into the next room, and found Geppetto working away busily at his wood-carver's bench. Everything was spick and span, and the tools were gleaming.

"This change for the better is all your doing," he told his son, giving him a hug. "When naughty boys turn over a new leaf, they make everything seem bright. Just look at that silly old puppet down there — aren't you glad you're no longer like that?"

Pinocchio looked down to see the crumpled wooden toy, leaning against a chair with its head on one side, and its arms dangling awkwardly. "How ridiculous I must have been," he thought to himself. Then he knelt down and set the puppet straight, and felt very proud to be real.

The End

Box of Robbers

Martha was all alone in the house and feeling very bored. "I know," she thought after a while, "I'll fetch my doll's house from the attic and play with that." So she climbed the stairs to the little room under the roof. Inside there were boxes and trunks, piles of old carpet, furniture and bundles of clothing. And in a dusty corner she found her doll's house.

Martha was about to pick it up, when she noticed the black wooden chest her Uncle Walter had sent from Italy. Martha had been told there was no key, and that Uncle Walter had forbidden anyone to open it.

It was a big chest, studded with big brass nails. Martha longed to see what was in it. "Oh, if only I had a key . . ." she thought. Then, she remembered the big basket of keys on the shelf in the linen cupboard. Perhaps one of them would unlock the mysterious chest?

Martha tried one key after another. At last, an ancient brass key slipped into the lock. Martha heard a click — and as the lid flew up, she jumped back in amazement.

Slowly and carefully, a man stepped out, stretched himself, then bowed to her politely. He was tall and thin and his face was suntanned.

Then, another man emerged from the chest, yawning. He was middle-sized, and his skin was as tanned as the first.

While Martha stared, open-mouthed, a third man crawled out of the chest. He had a suntan, too, but was short and fat.

And they all wore long, red velvet jackets, braided with gold, and sky-blue satin breeches. Their hats had broad brims and ribbons fluttered from the crowns. They had big, gold rings in their ears and knives and pistols in their belts. Their black eyes glittered, and they wore long, curling moustaches.

"My! You were heavy!" exclaimed the fat one. "You squeezed me out of shape."

"There's no need to be disagreeable," said the middle-sized man.

"Permit us to introduce ourselves," said the thin man to Martha. "This is Luigi," — the fat man nodded. "And this is Beni," — the middle-sized man bowed. "And I am Victor. We're Italian bandits."

"Bandits!" cried Martha, in horror.

"Perhaps in all the world there are

not three bandits more terrible and fierce," boasted Beni.

"That's true," said Luigi nodding.

"But . . . it's wicked!" cried Martha.

"You're right," said Victor. "We're extremely wicked."

"That's true," said Luigi nodding.

"But it's . . . it's naughty!" said Martha.

"Naughty?" gasped Beni with a horrified look. "I little thought to be called that — and by a lady! Oh! Oh! But how are we to be bandits, unless we're wicked?"

"Well, stop being bandits!"

Luigi sat down on an old chair and wiped his forehead with a yellow silk scarf. Beni and Victor stared at Martha with pale faces.

"But what shall we do for a living?" all three said.

"Oh there's lots to do. You could drive a bus or be a clerk — or, or become policemen."

"Policemen?" they said, shaking their heads. "But our business is to rob."

Martha tried to think. "I know it's hard, but you could try."

"No!" cried Beni. "Bandits we have always been and bandits we must remain! There are always people to rob!"

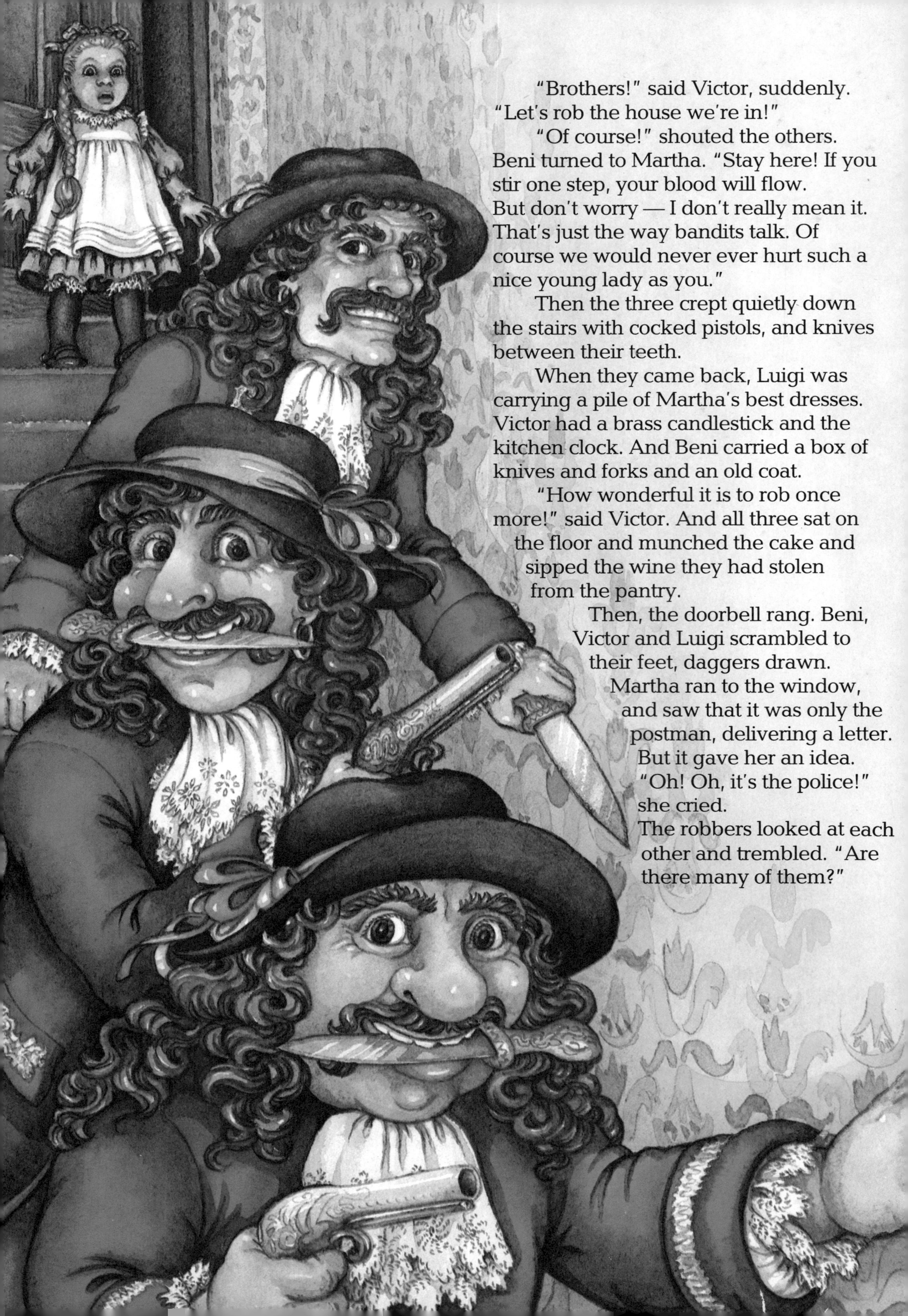

"Brothers!" said Victor, suddenly. "Let's rob the house we're in!"

"Of course!" shouted the others. Beni turned to Martha. "Stay here! If you stir one step, your blood will flow. But don't worry — I don't really mean it. That's just the way bandits talk. Of course we would never ever hurt such a nice young lady as you."

Then the three crept quietly down the stairs with cocked pistols, and knives between their teeth.

When they came back, Luigi was carrying a pile of Martha's best dresses. Victor had a brass candlestick and the kitchen clock. And Beni carried a box of knives and forks and an old coat.

"How wonderful it is to rob once more!" said Victor. And all three sat on the floor and munched the cake and sipped the wine they had stolen from the pantry.

Then, the doorbell rang. Beni, Victor and Luigi scrambled to their feet, daggers drawn.

Martha ran to the window, and saw that it was only the postman, delivering a letter. But it gave her an idea. "Oh! Oh, it's the police!" she cried.

The robbers looked at each other and trembled. "Are there many of them?"

I don't understand. Perhaps its those cakes we ate."

"Could be," answered Luigi's voice.

So Martha sat on the lid and pressed it down with all her weight. With a click the chest snapped shut. And with a broad, happy smile, Martha turned the old brass key.

Now this story should teach us not to interfere with things that do not concern us. Because if Martha had not opened Uncle Walter's chest, she would not have had to carry all the robber's plunder downstairs.

"A hundred and twelve!" exclaimed Martha after pretending to count.

"Then we are lost!" declared Beni. "Are they armed?"

"Oh yes," said Martha, "with guns and swords and pistols and axes and . . . and . . . cannons!"

All three groaned, but Beni said, "I hope they kill us quickly."

"You are my friends, aren't you?" said Martha turning from the window. "Then I shall save you. I suggest you get back into the chest. I'll close the lid, then the police won't find you. But you must be quick! They'll soon be here!"

Into the chest jumped Luigi, lying flat on the bottom. Next in went Beni and, pausing only to kiss Martha's hand, Victor lay on top. When they were all settled in, Martha pressed the lid down tightly. "Try pushing down more," she said. "Squeeze down more. Squeeze down."

"I'm doing my best," snapped Victor. "We fitted nicely before.

The Flying Piggy-Bank

My Mum gave me a smashing piggy-bank for my birthday. It was pink and round, with the word TAIWAN stamped on its underside in capital letters. I put it on the window-sill in my bedroom, and every week I put some of my pocket money through the slot on its back.

Then one day I decided I wanted to buy a new bed for my doll's house. I took down the piggy-bank, prised open the rubber plug underneath it and shook it hard over my bed.

Nothing came out. Not a penny.

"It's gone!" I shouted. "I've been putting money in here for weeks and it's all gone! Where's my money?"

"I ate it."

"What did you say?" I could hardly believe where the voice was coming from.

"You fed it to me, so I ate it," repeated the piggy-bank.

"Oh, you can talk, can you?"

"Yes, if someone talks to me."

"In that case you can tell me where my money is."

"I've told you, I ate it."

"But it's not in your stomach any more!"

"I've digested it," said Taiwan. "Where else do you think pigs like me get our energy from?"

"It's not good enough," I said, giving him another shake. "I want my poocket money! Give it back at once!"

"I can't" he said crossly. "We'll just have to go and get some more."

"Where from?" I asked.

"Well, where does money come from?" Taiwan said impatiently. "The Royal Mint, of course. The Royal Mint inside the Royal Palace of the Prince of Riches. If you climb on my back I'll fly you there. But you'll have to feed me first. I'm starving! And I can't fly on an empty stomach."

I fetched my collection of foreign coins and posted them into the slot.

With all this money the pig began to grow. He grew to such a size that he rolled off the window-sill, and soon a

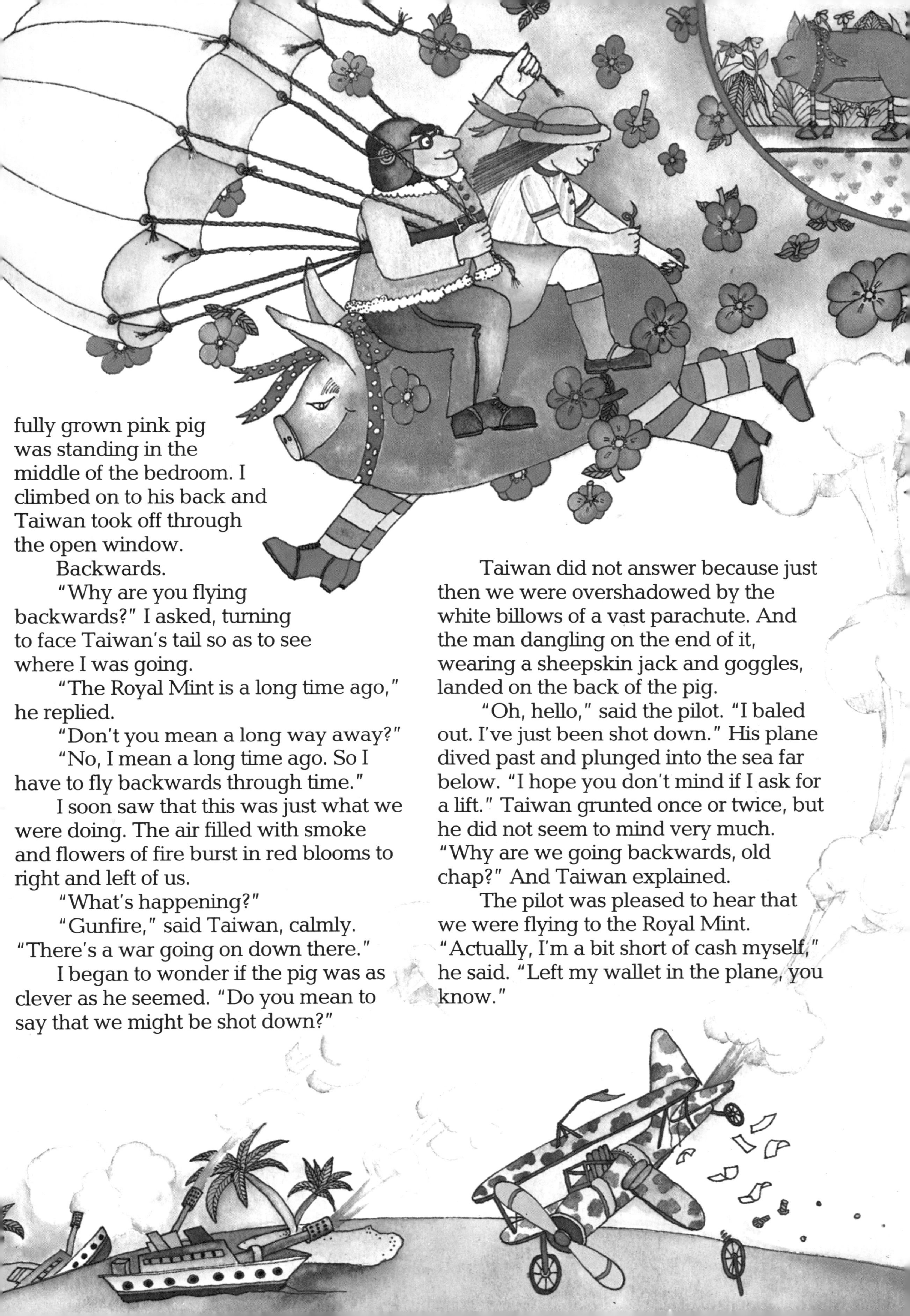

fully grown pink pig was standing in the middle of the bedroom. I climbed on to his back and Taiwan took off through the open window.

Backwards.

"Why are you flying backwards?" I asked, turning to face Taiwan's tail so as to see where I was going.

"The Royal Mint is a long time ago," he replied.

"Don't you mean a long way away?"

"No, I mean a long time ago. So I have to fly backwards through time."

I soon saw that this was just what we were doing. The air filled with smoke and flowers of fire burst in red blooms to right and left of us.

"What's happening?"

"Gunfire," said Taiwan, calmly. "There's a war going on down there."

I began to wonder if the pig was as clever as he seemed. "Do you mean to say that we might be shot down?"

Taiwan did not answer because just then we were overshadowed by the white billows of a vast parachute. And the man dangling on the end of it, wearing a sheepskin jack and goggles, landed on the back of the pig.

"Oh, hello," said the pilot. "I baled out. I've just been shot down." His plane dived past and plunged into the sea far below. "I hope you don't mind if I ask for a lift." Taiwan grunted once or twice, but he did not seem to mind very much. "Why are we going backwards, old chap?" And Taiwan explained.

The pilot was pleased to hear that we were flying to the Royal Mint. "Actually, I'm a bit short of cash myself," he said. "Left my wallet in the plane, you know."

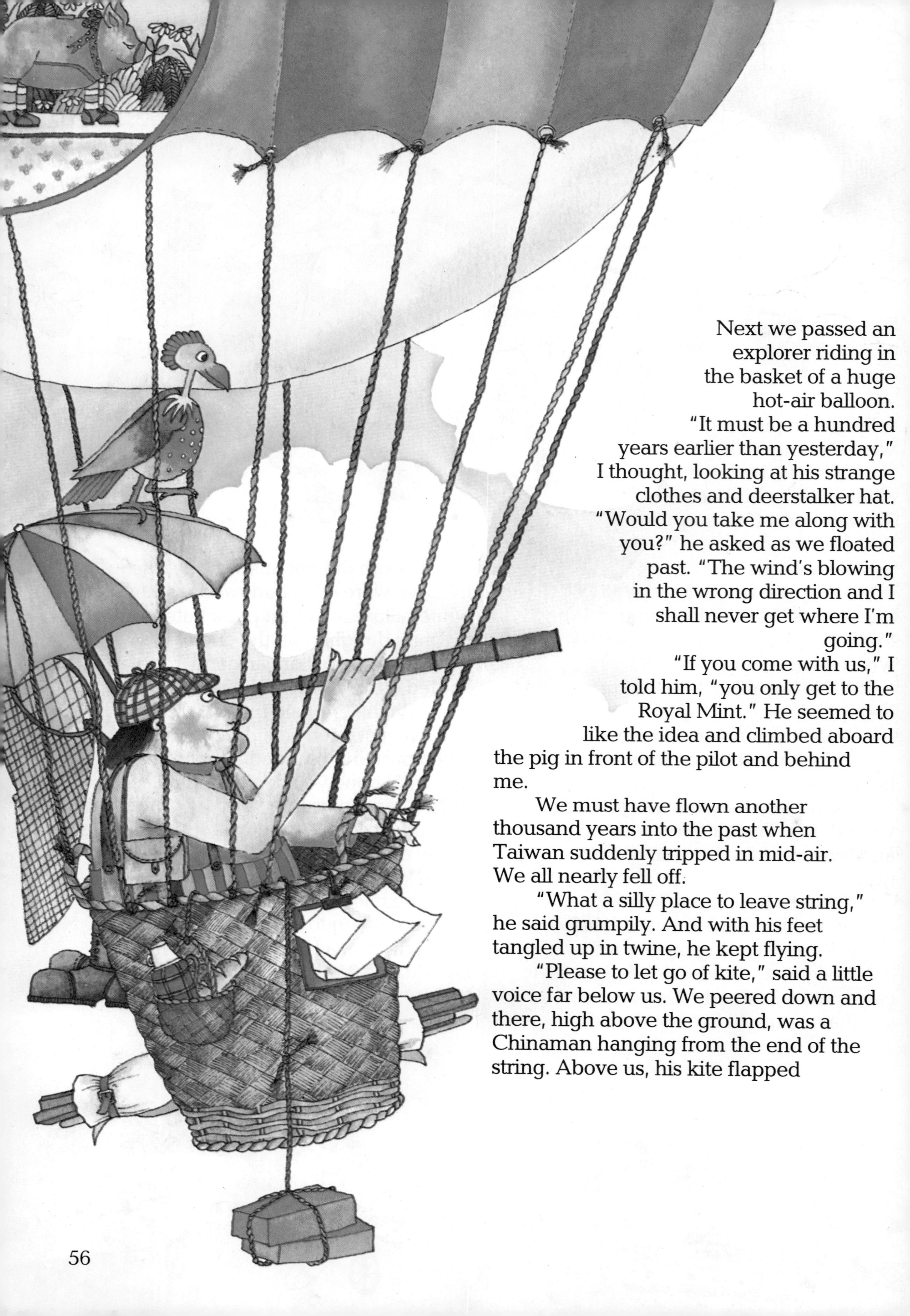

Next we passed an explorer riding in the basket of a huge hot-air balloon.

"It must be a hundred years earlier than yesterday," I thought, looking at his strange clothes and deerstalker hat.

"Would you take me along with you?" he asked as we floated past. "The wind's blowing in the wrong direction and I shall never get where I'm going."

"If you come with us," I told him, "you only get to the Royal Mint." He seemed to like the idea and climbed aboard the pig in front of the pilot and behind me.

We must have flown another thousand years into the past when Taiwan suddenly tripped in mid-air. We all nearly fell off.

"What a silly place to leave string," he said grumpily. And with his feet tangled up in twine, he kept flying.

"Please to let go of kite," said a little voice far below us. We peered down and there, high above the ground, was a Chinaman hanging from the end of the string. Above us, his kite flapped

like a bright paper bird. Taiwan had got caught up in an ancient Chinese kite.

"Why pig not look there where it is going?" asked the Chinaman as he climbed up the string and joined us on the pig's back. I explained that we were flying backwards through time. We all admired the kite and said how clever the Chinese had been to invent kites before anyone else. And our new passenger cheered up a lot.

"Chinese also invent banknotes," said the little man when we told him we were going in search of money. Taiwan shuddered: "I *never* eat paper money," he grunted.

We flew on, just beyond the start of Time, turned left, and the Palace of the Prince of riches appeared on the horizon.

The Royal Mint grew green and sweet-smelling against the Royal Back Wall of the palace. It was guarded by a large, royal cat with an arching back — but he was no match for a flying pig, a fighter pilot, an explorer, a Chinaman and of course me.

While they were struggling and scrambling through the Royal Sage and Thyme. I crept in among the Royal Mint and picked the silver and copper coins that hung down from every plant, and stuffed my pockets with them. When Taiwan trotted up I posted the coins into his slot and we all climbed aboard for the return journey.

We flew forwards this time, of course, the pig's ears crackling in the wind. But with four passengers aboard, Taiwan was soon tired and hungry again.

"More money! More money!" he grunted, and I posted a handful of coins into his slot.

"I'm sorry," he said shortly. "But some of you must get off. You're just too heavy for me."

"That's quite all right, said the explorer. "My hot-air balloon has just come into sight. Look, it's over there."

The pilot decided to join the explorer

in his travels round the world. And the Chinaman drifted back to earth on the end of his kite string. So I was left all alone, riding the flying pig. But before we reached home, I had to feed every coin I had picked at the Royal Mint into Taiwan's slot.

"I'm still hungry!" he complained, and his empty stomach rumbled between my knees. I shut my eyes and wedged my fingers into his slot in case we crashed.

The next thing I knew, we had tumbled in through my bedroom window and the pig was lying on its side on the floor, small and stiff and shrunken back to its normal size.

I picked it up and shook it. Not a rattle. I peered down its slot. Not a penny. I ran into the kitchen and shouted to my mother. "There's no money left in the piggy-bank!"

"Yes dear, I'm sorry about that," she said. "I had to borrow it to pay the milkman. "Let's see — how much was in there? Here you are."

She gave me two crisp green notes. I crinkled them in my hand, remembering that Taiwan did not eat paper money.

"Do you think that if I saved my pocket money every week . . ."

"Pigs might fly," said mother,

"Oh well," I said, "I will then!"

PETRUSHKA

The bells were ringing out all over Moscow. A mighty pealing chorus echoed far across the city. It was shrove Tuesday, the day of the great carnival.

Admiralty Square was packed with people, and there were entertainers everywhere — strongmen lifting massive bar-bells, bareback riders on nimble little ponies, sword-swallowers and fire-eaters, jugglers and dancers.

Most popular of all was a brightly coloured tent where a Showman was introducing his puppet show.

"The show you are about to witness, ladies and gentlemen, is a spectacle unmatched in all the Russias!" declared the Showman, his black eyes glinting beneath his fur hat. "The puppets you will see today are quite unlike any you have ever seen! They will come alive before your very eyes!"

With a flourish, the Showman flicked aside the curtain to reveal three magnificent puppets: the Moor a dashing Moroccan prince; the Princess, a delicate ballerina; and Petrushka, a wicked-looking sailor.

"They're not alive!" came a hoarse shout from the back of the crowd, where a fat merchant was winking at two gypsy girls. 'Tell us another one. Hah!"

But with a withering glance, the Showman pulled from his deep pocket a tiny silver flute and touched each puppet in turn

upon the shoulder. Instantly, they sprang to their feet, and as the Showman played a lively tune they danced and twisted about on the little stage.

At the end of the dance, the crowd cheered with delight — and with a loud guffaw, the merchant threw a pile of rouble notes high into the air! The gypsy girls jumped to catch them, but the Showman silenced everyone with a long, low note from the flute.

The puppets stood as if bewitched. Then the showman began playing a slow, mysterious tune and the Moor stood proudly at one side of the stage, his hands on his hips. The Princess stood in the centre, smiling radiantly, and Petrushka fell to his knees, as if pleading with her.

"The ugly sailor Petrushka loves the Princess," said the Showman. "But she rejects him."

The ballerina turned to the Moor and took his arm. They strolled together at the edge of the stage, looking deep into each other's eyes. Then, Petrushka, snarling like a tiger, pulled out a cudgel and ran across the stage. He tried to attack his rival, but the Moor bravely stepped in front of the Princess and knocked the cudgel from the sailor's hand.

Petrushka crawled back across the stage, then turned and begged for mercy. But the ballerina took the Moor's arm and walked with him to the centre of the stage. Ignoring poor Petrushka, they hugged each other and bowed deeply to the crowd.

"Thus the Moor marries the Princess and the sailor becomes their servant," boomed the showman, and he swept the curtain back across the stage. "The last show will be at four o'clock." Then he walked through the crowd, collecting coins in his fur hat.

The Showman sat down on a bench behind the theatre, and counted his money. It had been a good day, all right! Five shows already, and plenty of coins in the hat! He gave a deep, throaty chuckle, and closed his eyes for a nap.

But behind the curtain, in their dressing rooms, the puppets were stirring.

Petrushka the ugly sailor was in tears. "How I hate that Showman," he cried. "why did he make me so ugly, and the Princess so beautiful? If only I was handsome, like the Moor, or I could dance like him! Then perhaps she might love me instead!" Then perhaps she might love me instead!" He jerked to his feet and took a few, awkward steps towards the stage. "I must learn to dance, I must! Then I will kill the Moor, and marry the Princess.

At that moment Petrushka noticed the ballerina watching him from her room. She danced towards him on the tips of her toes, as graceful and as delicate as a bird. Petrushka's heart pounded, and he tried desperately to dance beside her, but it was no good. He tripped over his feet and fell to the floor.

The ballerina soon got bored with watching his clumsy efforts. So she danced away again, along the stage.

The Moor in his dressing room was practising with his scimitar in front of a mirror. He strode manfully up and down, and cut and slashed and lunged. But when the ballerina danced in, the Moor sprang to attention. He clapped merrily

and stamped his feet
as she glided
towards him.
Then they spun
around together
in a wild, Eastern
dance.

Suddenly
Petrushka burst in. He had
been watching them from
the stage and he could not bear to see his
beloved ballerina dancing with the Moor.
"Take your hands off my Princess!" he
shouted. And he charged at the Moor,
brandishing his cudgel.

Outside the theatre, a crowd was
gathering for the last show of the day.
The golden domes threw long shadows
across the square, but many people had
stayed late to see the famous puppet
show. The merchant was back again,
with his two gypsy girls, and there was
even a performing bear
with his trainer! They all
gathered in a semi-circle
and waited patiently while
the Showman recited his speech:

"Ladies and gentlemen, the
puppets you will see today are
unlike any you have ever seen.
They will come alive before your . . ."

But, at that moment, the curtains
burst open behind the Showman's back.
Petrushka leaped down from the stage
and ran away full pelt across the square.
Behind him rushed the Moor, in a furious
rage, waving the scimitar above his head.
As the crowd turned in astonishment,
Petrushka slipped and fell. Down came
the scimitar in a great, flashing arc, and
Petrushka lay deadly still, face down in
the snow.

"They're alive!" shouted the merchant. There's been a murder!"

But the Showman snatched up the Moor and Petrushka, and shook and slapped them. A trail of sawdust trickled down from Petrushka's face. "There you are," he whined. "Just puppets. But there'll be no more shows today, ladies and gentleman."

As the crowd drifted away, the Showman thrust the two puppets in through the back of the theatre and closed the tent. Then he walked off to a tavern, shaking his head gloomily.

Later that night he returned to the theatre. He drew back the curtain, and peered inside. There was the ballerina, sleeping in her room. The Moor sat cross-legged on the stage, quitely polishing his scimitar. On the floor lay Petrushka, broken and torn.

"What was that?" gasped the Showman. Something was moving in the darkness above the theatre. He looked up and saw in the moonlight — the ghost of Petrushka, dancing in the air. It shook its fist and scowled at the Showman.

"You made me ugly!" it snarled. "You made a fool of me! But now it's my turn, I'm free of the body you made for me. Now I can dance as well as anyone. Watch me! My love for the ballerina has made my spirit delicate and free. But my ugliness will haunt you for the rest of your days! And his laughter echoed in the frosty air.